P · O · C · K · E · T · S

BUILDINGS

CHRYSLER
BUILDING,
NEW YORK

WAT SORASAK,
SUKHOTHAI,
THAILAND

CRUCK-FRAMED
HOUSE

P·O·C·K·E·T·S

BUILDINGS

Written by
PHILIP WILKINSON

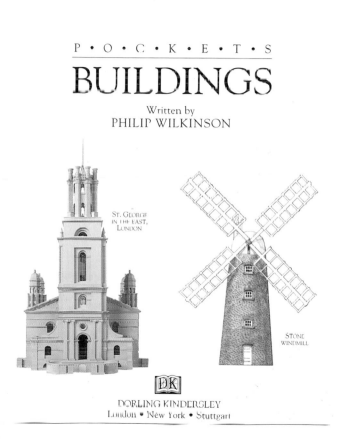

ST. GEORGE
IN THE EAST,
LONDON

STONE
WINDMILL

DK

DORLING KINDERSLEY
London • New York • Stuttgart

A DORLING KINDERSLEY BOOK

Editor Suzanne Melia
Neil Bridges
Art editor Heather Blackham
Senior editor Susan McKeever
Senior art editor Helen Senior
Picture research Caroline Brooke
Production Louise Barratt
Consultant Cany Ash

First published in Great Britain in 1995
by Dorling Kindersley Limited
9 Henrietta Street, Covent Garden, London WC2E 8PS

A CIP catalogue record for this book is available from
the British Library

ISBN 0 7513 5180 6

Colour reproduction by Colourscan, Singapore
Printed and bound in Italy by L.E.G.O.

CONTENTS

HOW TO USE THIS BOOK

These pages show you how to use *Pockets: Buildings*.
The book is divided into several historical sections,
covering the most important architectural styles
and building techniques of that period. There is
an introductory section at the front, and a reference
section at the back. Each section begins with
a picture page.

HISTORICAL PERIODS
The buildings in this book are
arranged according to the time
they were built. In each historical
section, you will find information
on the most important styles of
architecture and examples of
outstanding buildings of the time.

Corner coding

Heading

Introduction

Label

Feature box

THE EUROPEAN RENAISSANCE

FRENCH RENAISSANCE

THE RENAISSANCE CAME later to France than it did to
Italy. The first French Renaissance buildings were
designed in the 16th century, and often show a
combination of Gothic and classical details. Square-
headed windows, steeply sloping roofs, and a restrained
use of ornament are the
trademarks of the style.

FRENCH WINDOWS
These were often square-headed,
with wings bearing a foliage or
looped draperies. Curved-headed
windows followed later.

PARISIAN CHURCH
French Renaissance
buildings often show a
mixture of styles. This
church in Paris has a
rose window, like those
in some Gothic
churches, and a delicate
rood screen (the
balcony holding the
crucifix). The curved
pediment is a typical
Renaissance feature.

Caption

CORNER CODING
Corners of the pages
are colour coded to
remind you which
historical section
you are in.

☐ EARLY
CIVILIZATIONS

☐ MEDIEVAL
BUILDINGS

☐ THE EUROPEAN
RENAISSANCE

☐ THE
INDUSTRIAL AGE

☐ MODERN
ARCHITECTURE

HEADING
This describes the
subject of the page.
This page is about the
French Renaissance. If
a subject continues
over several pages, the
same heading applies.

INTRODUCTION
This provides a clear,
general overview of the
subject. After reading
this, you should have
an idea of what the
pages are about.

CAPTIONS AND
ANNOTATIONS
Each illustration has a
caption. Annotations, in
italics, point out features
of an illustration and
usually have leader lines.

RUNNING HEADS
These remind you which section you are in. The left-hand page gives the section name. The right-hand page gives the subject. This page on the French Renaissance is in The European Renaissance section.

FACT BOXES
Many pages have a fact box. These contain at-a-glance information about the subject. This fact box gives details, such as how many people once lived in the Palace of Versailles.

FEATURES
These allow a closer look at a decorative detail, such as a carved doorway or column, or a glimpse of an unusual feature that we might not normally see.

Running head   *Fact box*

Annotation

REFERENCE SECTION
The reference section pages are yellow and appear at the back of the book. On these, you will find useful facts, figures, and charts. These pages describe some of the main components of architecture, such as domes, roofs, and arches, and contain a list of famous architects and their buildings.

LABELS
For extra clarity, some pictures have labels. They may provide extra information, or identify a picture when it is not obvious from the text. A label helps to locate each building.

INDEX
At the back of the book, an easy-to-use index lists the main subjects, buildings, and architects in alphabetical order. The index is a fast, direct route to a specific person, building, or style of architecture.

INTRODUCTION
TO BUILDINGS

THE FIRST BUILDINGS

PEOPLE HAVE ALWAYS NEEDED shelter from the elements, and very early in human history our ancestors began to construct buildings to live in. They used whatever materials were to hand, such as wood, earth, stone, and animal skins. Basic structures soon evolved with wooden frames, or solid walls of mud or stone.

BRUSHWOOD HUT
About 380,000 years ago, our ancestors created simple shelters out of closely packed brushwood held in place by rocks. Huts like these were only occupied for part of the year. People moved about often to search for food.

Rocks held the structure in place.

These huts in Chile are the earliest known dwellings in the Americas.

Fire pit   *Animal skins*

WOODEN DWELLINGS
Rows of wooden-framed huts were built in Monte Verde, Chile, in c.12,000 B.C. The frames were covered in animal skins, and pits were sunk into the floors for fires.

The stone walls, sunk partially into the ground, provided a permanent structure.

ROUND HOUSE, AIN MALLAHA, ISRAEL

Stone wall

FACTS AND FIGURES

• The first houses evolved from temporary tent-like structures.

• Woolly mammoth bones were used as frames by early builders in the Ukraine and Siberia.

• The remains of several Neanderthal huts were found inside a cave in France.

ROUND HOUSE
The inhabitants of coastal Israel, Syria, and Lebanon built round houses like this one in c 10,000 B.C. These houses were built by people who stayed in one place, gathering wild food.

Cross-section showing sunken interior.

THE FIRST TOWNS
By c.6000 B.C., early towns, like Çatal Hüyük in Turkey, were being built. Their mud-brick houses nestled close together. Access was through trapdoors in the flat roofs, which could be used as work areas when it was not too hot.

SETTLEMENT, ÇATAL HÜYÜK, TURKEY

Ladders lead from the roofs down into the buildings.

Flat roof

Yard

13

WHAT IS ARCHITECTURE?

THE FIRST SIMPLE SHELTERS and houses were built by
the people who lived in them. But for larger or more
complex structures, such as temples, public buildings,
and royal palaces, the process must be planned. These
buildings are designed by an
architect to be functional,
attractive, and comfortable. The
site is prepared, the materials
ordered, and a workforce
organized. Architects often have
their own distinctive style.

STONEMASON
Some of the most
important workers on a
Roman building site were
the masons. Later, during
the medieval period, the
master mason played the
role of architect.

*This temple to the Sun
god Ra was dominated by
a huge stone obelisk.*

Altar

Open
courtyard

TEMPLE OF RA,
EGYPT

Causeway

Second
temple

EGYPTIAN TEMPLE
One of the first architects we know is Imhotep, designer
of the first pyramid. The Egyptians produced some of the
biggest buildings of the ancient world. Building temples,
like this one at Abu Ghurab, involved the transport of
huge amounts of stone by a large workforce.

SUNDIAL, REIMS CATHEDRAL

Buildings usually do more than just provide shelter. Even the humblest house will have some decoration that reflects the taste of its builder or owner. The sundial on this French cathedral is a functional piece of decoration which also tells worshippers when it is time for mass.

GARGOYLES

The gargoyles on Gothic cathedrals are guardians against evil spirits, and are often carved in a style quite at odds with the rest of the building.

Gargoyles cover water spouts

ART GALLERY

Architects often become as famous as their buildings. This art museum was designed by Frank Lloyd Wright. Visitors take a lift to the top, then walk down a long spiral ramp to view the pictures. The distinctive form of the ramp is visible from the outside.

GUGGENHEIM MUSEUM, NEW YORK

The concrete circles and spirals are in contrast to the surrounding buildings.

Spiral ramp

THE SOLOMON R. GUGGENHEIM MUSEUM

BUILDING FOR PEOPLE

ALTHOUGH TRENDS IN architecture are often set by large public buildings or specifically commissioned houses, most of the buildings in the world are smaller structures – people's homes, which sometimes also double as their places of work. Most houses consist of walls and a roof in various styles.

Homes and workplaces

Homes vary greatly around the world, depending on the climate and the environment. If an area is prone to flooding, for example, houses may be built on stilts; in a desert, thick walls will keep a house cool during the day, but warm at night.

Thatch

Timber frame

Stilt

STILT HOUSE,
THAILAND

FACTS AND FIGURES

• Longhouses can be 45 m (150 ft) in length.

• In the hot Australian desert, some houses have been built underground.

• Elegant terraces were built in towns in the 18th century to house the wealthy.

• The Industrial Age saw many more houses being put up by professional builders.

STILT HOUSE

Raised on poles to keep it away from the floods of the rainy season, this Thai house is made of wood and thatch. Houses like this have been built in Southeast Asia for hundreds of years.

Wattle and daub wall

Thatched roof

LONGHOUSE, BYLANY, MORAVIA

Wooden sails

Cap

STONE WINDMILL

TIMBER LONGHOUSE

People sometimes occupied one end of a house, and their animals the other. This central European longhouse has a timber framework and wattle and daub (woven twigs plastered with clay) walls.

WINDMILL

Some buildings are designed for a very specialized function. The sails of a windmill are mounted on a cap which can be turned into the wind.

GREAT CUMBERLAND PLACE, LONDON, ENGLAND

WESTERN TOWN HOUSE

In the limited space of cities, more room can be made by building high. In this way the requirements of the rich, including the servants' rooms in the attic and the kitchens in the basement, could be fitted into a tall, elegant house. This terrace in London was built in 1790.

Public buildings

Temples, churches, assembly halls, and places of government are often some of the most interesting buildings. Designed to be used by large groups of people, they can be large and complex, sometimes with many rooms arranged around a large central hall. Public buildings are often adorned with decoration that reflects their use – a senate house, for example, may have statues representing justice or democracy.

House of Lords

Central lobby

Clock tower

House of Commons

Member's entrance

HOUSES OF PARLIAMENT, LONDON, ENGLAND

GOVERNMENT BUILDINGS
Modern government buildings are vast complexes that must meet several needs. As well as debating chambers, the Houses of Parliament in London contain offices, lobbies, libraries, restaurants, and committee rooms.

Royal
Gallery

This large complex in Rome contained public libraries, galleries, and gardens.

BATHS OF
CARACALLA,
ROME

ROMAN BATHS
In ancient Rome, people gathered in large public baths. Here people met, did business, and socialized, as well as bathing in communal hot and cold rooms.

Since Islam forbids figurative art, the main decorations in a mosque are abstract patterns.

SULTAN HASSAN MOSQUE
Inside a mosque, the main space is the prayer hall, which is often a large, high-ceilinged room like this one in Rabat, Morocco.

Minaret

Wall inlaid
with tiles

FRIDAY MOSQUE
Public buildings often proclaim their purpose from afar. Mosques like this one in Isfahan, Iran have tall towers, or minarets, from which the faithful can be called to prayer.

Entrance arch

Carved wood and plaster decorate the prayer hall

Special-purpose buildings

CAERNARVON
CASTLE,
WALES

An architect needs to think carefully about how a new building is going to be used. This is the case in the smallest, most straightforward house, but it is even more obvious in the host of buildings designed for a more specific purpose. A railway station, for example, will need a large train shed and spacious areas in which passengers can move around. A concert hall will need a variety of backstage facilities, from dressing rooms to store-rooms – often larger than the auditorium itself.

Arrow-slits

MEDIEVAL CASTLE
Medieval castles have thick walls for protection. Towers with arrow-slits and battlements allow the defenders to fire at the enemy while remaining hidden.

AIRPORT TERMINAL
Architects sometimes use form and structure to suggest the purpose of their buildings. Eero Saarinen's passenger terminal at Kennedy Airport in New York (finished in 1962) is roofed by a concrete shell that suggests a soaring bird.

Concrete roof

Roof support

Large windows

TWA TERMINAL, NEW YORK, U.S.A.

The ceiling is painted to look like the sky.

TEATRO OLIMPICO

Renaissance architect Andrea Palladio drew on ancient Roman theatre design in this late 16th-century building. He also built elaborate permanent scenery to resemble a real street scene. The scenery was designed to portray an ideal city of the Renaissance.

Statues overlook the auditorium

The audience sit on tiered seats in front of the stage.

Permanent stage setting of classical architecture

The area in front of the stage is called the orchestra

Horseshoe-shaped auditorium

Curving concrete ramp

PENGUIN POOL, LONDON ZOO, ENGLAND

PENGUIN POOL

Designing buildings for animals has its own special problems. In the 1930s, Berthold Lubetkin used concrete's special sculptural qualities to create an environment in which the penguins of London Zoo would feel at home.

MATERIALS

THE EARLIEST BUILDINGS were made of naturally occurring materials, such as wood, stone, and grass. But, about 6,000 years ago, people learned to bake clay bricks. Today, buildings combine natural and manufactured materials.

WOOD
Timber is widely used for roof frameworks, floors, and window frames. Trees are specially planted to supply timber for building.

Thatched roof

Lath

Rafter

Hazel rod

Layer of thatch

GRASS
Straw from grasses or reeds is one of the oldest roofing materials. It is used for lightweight roofing in Africa, and thick waterproof coverings in Europe.

SLATES
A common roofing material, slate is a stone that can be split into thin sheets, then nailed onto wooden rafters.

Modern slate

Granite

STONE
From hard, durable granite to the softer limestones that can be cut and carved, stone is one of the oldest and most resilient of the building materials.

BRICK
Earth pressed into moulds and baked in the sun or in a kiln produces bricks. Simple to lay, and very long-lasting, bricks have been used for thousands of years.

Modern engineering brick

Glass

GLASS
For centuries glass was an expensive luxury that could only be made in small pieces. Medieval stained-glass makers used these small pieces in their designs. It was only in the 19th century that glass could be produced in large sheets.

Lead frame

Coarse

Medium-coarse

Fine texture

CONCRETE
The Romans invented concrete and used it extensively. This mixture of sand, gravel, and cement was not used again until the 18th century.

METAL
The Industrial Revolution of the 18th and 19th centuries saw an increase in the use of metal in buildings. Iron pillars and steel frameworks held up buildings from warehouses to office blocks.

The use of iron and steel enabled the construction of multi-storey buildings.

STRUCTURE

WHATEVER MATERIALS are used, whether natural or manufactured, buildings have two basic types of structure. They can either be frame buildings, with a sturdy, skeleton-like frame holding up the roof, or solid buildings, with heavy walls taking the weight of the entire structure.

FRAME BUILDING
Timber-framed buildings were common in 16th-century Europe.

The roof is a wooden-framed structure covered with tiles.

Part of timber frame

TIMBER FRAME
A frame building has a framework that bears the weight and is filled in with a non-load-bearing material. This medieval house has a wooden frame. The gaps in the walls would have been filled with wattle (woven wooden strips called laths) and daub (a mixture of clay and dung).

Panel of wattle and daub

Floorboards

Staircase

SOLID WALL AND FRAME ROOF

Many small buildings have solid walls and a frame roof. This corner of a small house shows a solid wall of bricks, and a roof consisting of a wooden framework covered in plain tiles.

Frame roof is light and easy to build

ROOF TYPES

The simplest roof designs are the hipped and pavilion, with sloping ends. More complex layouts, like the gable-and valley or sloped turret, are used on ornate buildings.

GABLE-AND-VALLEY

PAVILION

SLOPED TURRET

HIPPED

Concrete dome

PANTHEON, ROME

Brick-and-concrete walls

SOLID BUILDING

In a solid building, the entire wall bears the weight of the structure. The Pantheon in Rome, Italy, is a solid building with walls of brick faced concrete and a solid domed roof. A system of buttresses (supports) also help to hold up the building.

Granite columns at entrance

EARLY CIVILIZATIONS

INTRODUCTION

AROUND 8000 B.C., people began to live together in towns and cities. These were often ruled by powerful leaders who lived in palaces. There was usually some form of organized religion, which meant that temples had to be built. The palace and the temple were the largest buildings in early cities. Strong walls with fortified gatehouses and watchtowers defended the cities from invasion.

Internal staircase

STONE TOWER, JERICHO, ISRAEL

Stone wall

STONE TOWER
Jericho was one of the first cities. Building began in c.8000 B.C., and the city was surrounded with a ditch and a wall topped with this stone tower.

CLAY TABLET
The development of writing has enabled us to learn much about early people and their buildings.

TEMPLE
The cities of Mesopotamia (modern Iraq) flourished after c.4300 B.C. The niches along the walls of this temple are typical of the period c.4300-3100 B.C.

TEMPLE, UQAIR, IRAQ

Main temple

Painted frieze

STONE GATEWAY

The Hittites flourished in Anatolia (modern Turkey) between the 14th and 12th centuries B.C. This stone gate remains from the capital at Hattushash (modern Boghazköy).

ENTRANCE GATE, BOGHAZKÖY, TURKEY

Rammed earth wall

Courtyard

Main hall

Stone lion

SHANG PALACE, CHINA

SHANG PALACE

The Shang civilization reached a high point in China in c.1600-1027 B.C. This typical Shang palace has a large one-room hall with a thatched gallery.

Timber doors

Thatched gallery

GRECIAN VASE

Pottery provides a good way of dating ancient buildings. This Greek vase is in the red-figure style, and dates from the period c.470-60 B.C.

VASE FROM ANCIENT GREECE

FACTS AND FIGURES

• Hittite houses had clay drainpipes.

• The Egyptians transported granite down the River Nile.

• Kings of Babylon had their names stamped on individual bricks.

• The Hittites built stone walls without using mortar.

MESOPOTAMIA

SOME OF THE MOST IMPORTANT early civilizations developed in Iraq after c. 4300 B.C. They were based around the Tigris and Euphrates rivers, in an area known as Mesopotamia. A series of city-states evolved, some of which expanded into empires. Mud bricks moulded from straw and mud were used to build everything from houses to temples.

ASSYRIAN DECORATION
The temples and palaces of the Assyrians (from the northern part of Mesopotamia) were decorated with carved stone reliefs, featuring winged figures and mythical beasts. They appeared on doorways and gates as protection.

STONE FIGURE   TERRACOTTA RELIEF

ZIGGURAT
This Sumerian temple at Ur was the first of many to be built in Mesopotamia. It dates from c. 2100 B.C., and consists of a series of stepped platforms made of mud bricks. It was designed to bring the priests closer to the heavens.

The temple was dedicated to the moon god.

Niches decorated the temple walls

ZIGGURAT AT UR

Stepped platform

ISHTAR GATE, IRAQ

Glazed bricks

- The floodplains of the rivers supplied the mud for making bricks.

- The Sumerians of southern Mesopotamia were the first people to settle in the region.

- The Assyrians, who ruled the largest empire, moved and rebuilt their capital city several times.

ISHTAR GATE

The city of Babylon dominated the region in the 6th century B.C. It was heavily fortified. This strong gatehouse is adorned with coloured glazed bricks showing animal symbols of Babylonian gods on a blue background.

CITY OF KHORSABAD

Khorsabad was one of the capital cities of the Assyrians, who ruled the region from the 9th to 7th centuries B.C. The large mud-brick city contained a palace and temple complex with a tall ziggurat. The Assyrians were often involved in wars, so the city was protected from invasion by strong walls and towers

Palace complex

ANCIENT EGYPT

THE ANCIENT Egyptians built the first large-scale stone buildings. Many of these were tombs. Egyptian pharaohs (kings) were often buried in massive stone pyramids, which took years to construct. Egyptians also built stone temples to their gods.

PYRAMIDS
The pharaohs of the Old Kingdom (c.2815-2294 B.C.) were buried in pyramids. The Step Pyramid is the earliest. The "Bent" Pyramid and the Great Pyramid followed.

STEP PYRAMID | "BENT" PYRAMID (2723 B.C.) | GREAT PYRAMID (2528 B.C.)

Sacred inscriptions on columns

TEMPLE OF AMON-RE
The main hall contains 134 columns decorated with hieroglyphs (picture writing) and paintings of gods and kings. The central nave (aisle) of the hall is about 24 m (79 ft) high.

TEMPLE OF LUXOR

TEMPLE OF LUXOR
This statue of Ramesses II dates from 1290-1220 B.C. It is one of two identical statues that flank the entrance to the temple. The Great Colonnade, behind, rises over 20 m (65 ft).

CLIFF-FACE TEMPLE

King Ramesses II's temple at Abu Simbel was carved out of a cliff face in c.1301 B.C. The front is decorated with four colossal statues of the king which are about 21 m (69 ft) high. Statues of the king's relatives stand at his feet.

GREAT PYRAMID, GIZA

This is the largest pyramid of all. It was originally 146.4 m (480 ft) high. The Great Pyramid has several chambers and is made mainly of limestone, with some granite.

King's burial chamber

Limestone facing

Temple for offerings

THE EAST

ANCIENT CHINESE and Japanese
buildings traditionally stand on a low
stone platform. Timber columns
support a heavy tiled roof. The space
between the supporting columns is filled with
thick outer walls or light lattice screens.

DECORATED
CHINESE ROOF

Ancient China

Chinese architecture changed little
from the Han Dynasty (206 B.C.-
A.D. 220) to the 19th century. Typical
Chinese buildings were timber-framed.
These roofs were decorated with
ornamental crests and upturned
corners, and often had coloured tiles.

WOODEN
PAGODA,
CHINA

Tiled roof with
upturned
corners

Stone
base

MULTI-STOREY TOWER
A pagoda is a many-sided, multi-storey
building with an odd number of floors.
Each storey has an ornamented
overhanging roof. The first pagodas were
wooden, but most that survive are of brick.

HAN DYNASTY HOUSE
A few original buildings survive
from the Han Dynasty period. They
are simple structures made of
rammed (packed) earth, but many
also featured the typical Chinese
overhanging roofs. This is a pottery
model of an ancient Chinese house.

INTERIOR, TEMPLE OF HEAVEN

SUPPORTING PILLARS
The largest of the three roofs of the Temple of Heaven is shown in this picture. It has 12 supporting pillars, each made from the trunk of a single tree.

FACTS AND FIGURES

• Bamboo frameworks supported the roofs.

• A system of rituals, called *feng shui*, influenced the design of a new building.

• The introduction of Buddhism in A.D. 65 influenced the Chinese pagoda style.

• Almost 1,000 buildings form the Forbidden City in Beijing, China.

TEMPLE OF HEAVEN
The Temple of Heaven in Beijing is a circular temple that dates from the 15th century. It was built for the emperor, who performed rituals of spirit worship on behalf of his people. The temple has three roofs covered with blue glazed tiles. Its interior is carved and painted, and the ceilings have coffers (sunken panels).

Gold-plated ornamental ball

The roof was the most important part of a traditional Chinese building. It was designed before the main structure of the building itself.

Each of the three circular roofs is covered with blue glazed tiles.

Load-bearing wooden framework

Brightly painted beams

Stone platform

Chinese imperial buildings

The emperors of China controlled a vast workforce and were able to build on a large scale. One grand imperial project was the Great Wall, begun by the First Emperor in about 214 B.C. Later emperors built fine capital cities. The emperors of the Ming Dynasty (1368-1644) chose Peking (now called Beijing) as their capital. It was the last and most important of the imperial cities.

The Meridian Gate was used only by the emperor.

FORBIDDEN CITY

As a capital, Peking was designed in zones. The inner area, the imperial court, was walled off from the rest of the city. The imperial court contained the emperor's quarters and buildings, such as temples, workshops, and stables. Only the imperial household and those on imperial business were allowed into the court. As a result, it was known as the "Forbidden City".

Walls separated the imperial court from the rest of Peking.

AUDIENCE HALLS

The Forbidden City is built around a series of audience halls in which the emperor received visitors. The halls are timber buildings raised on stone platforms and supported by wooden pillars. Inside, they are brightly decorated with carved and painted woodwork. In the middle of each hall was the emperor's throne.

The Hall of Supreme Harmony is the largest hall in the Forbidden City.

Hall of Complete Harmony

Hall of Preserving Harmony

Palace of Heavenly Purity

The buildings are timber framed. The wood came from forests about 1,500 km (932 miles) away from Peking.

Yellow roof tiles

Ornamented roof ridge

Canals criss-cross the city.

PALACE OF HEAVENLY PURITY
This palace in the Forbidden City has broad, overhanging roofs with yellow tiles. Yellow was a colour used only on buildings for the emperor.

Ancient Japan

Typical Japanese architecture developed slowly, and has changed little over the centuries. The style is influenced by climate, religion, and locally available materials, such as wood, paper, clay, and metals. Wood-framed buildings have overhanging roofs to throw off the rain and to provide shade. Structures are often raised on platforms, and walls can be opened to allow air to circulate.

The irregular design of this roof is unusual.

PAGODA, YAKUSHI-JI
Pagodas dominate many Japanese Buddhist sites. Their tapering height reminds Buddhists of the sacred mythical Mount Meru.

GOLDEN HALL
Japan's oldest Buddhist temple at Nara was built in C.A.D. 607. This is the large central hall, used for prayer and teaching. Its gently curving tiled roofs and bracketed pillars are influenced by Chinese design.

Railings with decorative carving.

Curving tiled roof

HORYU-JI TEMPLE, NARA

Bracketed pillar

ORNATE SHRINE

A close look at the corner of a shrine shows some of the common features of Japanese construction. The main framework is made of wood, with the gaps between filled with lightweight sliding screens, thin walls, and doors. Ornately carved, brightly painted wooden brackets support the overhanging tiled roof.

HEIAN JINGU SHRINE, KYOTO

Wooden brackets

TOSHŌGU SHRINE

Shinto is the ancient religion of Japan, and this Shinto shrine at Nikko is over 1,000 years old. Its walls and roof show the ornate decoration painted on Japanese religious buildings. On the right is the Kara Mon Gate – a wooden gatehouse set on a massive stone base.

TOSHŌGU SHRINE, NIKKO

Kara Mon Gate

FACTS AND FIGURES

• Hollowed bamboo was used to make gutters and drainpipes.

• Timber buildings were less vulnerable to earthquakes.

• In Japanese houses, walls of translucent paper allow daylight to filter through.

• Japanese pagodas vary from three to fifteen storeys, and may be as high as 34 m (120 ft)

Japanese castles

During the 16th century, local lords called daimyo became very powerful in Japan. They built strong castles as military bases and homes for themselves and their followers, warriors known as samurai. These castles had a distinctive style. They usually had a central multi-storey keep, or donjon, made of wood. The keep stood on a stone base and was surrounded by a network of defensive stone walls and a moat.

SAMURAI

HIMEJI CASTLE

Originally built in medieval times, Himeji is one of the finest Japanese castles. It was extended and strengthened in the early 17th century. The walls of the keep had gun loops through which defenders fired guns. Defenders could also open hidden trapdoors and throw missiles onto the enemy below.

Decorated gable

White plaster walls

Courtyard

ROOFTOPS

Fine roofs were a status symbol in Japan. The decorated gables (triangular part of a wall enclosed by a sloping roof) and roofs of Himeji Castle show that an important lord lived there.

Outer courtyard

PLAN OF HIMEJI CASTLE
The keep is surrounded by several
courtyards, which are separated by stone
walls and gates. An enemy would have
to pass through all these courtyards to
reach the keep which was the safest
place to be during a siege.

Courtyards

Moat

Central keep

Decorated
roof

Timber-framed
rooms are typical
of the castle

Gun
loop

Side towers
give good
views over
courtyards.

Defensive
stone wall

Hidden
trapdoors

Gates guard the
entrances to the main
part of the castle.

MINOANS AND MYCENAEANS

THE MINOANS LIVED on Crete, an island in the Aegean Sea. Their kings lived in large, elegant palaces, the most famous of which is the palace of Minos at Knossos. The Mycenaean culture was based around citadels (fortified cities) on the mainland of Greece. Mycenae was the home of Agamemnon, a king in Greek mythology.

CYPRESS WOOD COLUMNS
Many rooms in the palace of Minos open on to courtyards that are surrounded by columns of cypress wood.

PALACE OF MINOS
This was the largest and most complex of the Minoan palaces. It was built over a long period and rooms seem to have been added as needed. The rooms were grouped around a central courtyard. Beautiful wall paintings called frescoes decorated many of these rooms.

PLAN OF THE PALACE OF MINOS, KNOSSOS

Central courtyard

Corridors and rooms with flat roofs

Cypress wood columns

LION GATE
Strong stone walls surround the palace at Mycenae. The main gate of the palace is topped by a 4.9 m-high (16-ft) lintel, a horizontal cover over an opening. A relief (wall carving) showing two lions separated by a column stands on top of the lintel. The gate was built in about 1250 B.C. and is known as the "Lion Gate".

UNDERGROUND TOMB
The Treasury of Atreus dates from about 1325 B.C. This Mycenaean tomb was built by digging a circular pit, lining this with stone blocks, and then cutting the stone to make a smooth interior surface. It has one of the most impressive early domes.

Capstone

Carved bands of chevrons

Limtel

COLUMN
This engraving shows one of the two columns at the entrance to the Treasury of Atreus.

Entrance to the tomb

Dome lined with stone

Burial chamber

CLASSICAL GREECE

THE GREEKS OF the classical period developed an elegant style of architecture with three main orders or styles. Each order had a different design for its columns, capitals, and entablatures (the structures above the capitals). These features are best seen in the Greek temples.

CARYATID ON
ERECHTHEION

CAPITALS

A Doric order column is topped with plain capitals. Ionic order capitals include decorative spiral scrolls, and capitals of the Corinthian order feature carved acanthus leaves.

DORIC   IONIC   CORINTHIAN

ERECHTHEION

The Acropolis (high city) overlooks Athens. One of its temples, shown in its original form in this etching, was the Erechtheion which was built between 421 and 405 B.C. Most of the columns are Ionic, although on one porch there are caryatids, columns in the shape of female figures.

FACTS AND FIGURES

• The classical period in Greece lasted from about 480 to 323 B.C.

• The three main Greek orders are Doric, Ionic, and Corinthian.

• Greek columns from the classical period appear to be straight, but are subtly curved.

• The stones that make up the Parthenon are joined together with wooden plugs.

SIDE VIEW OF
ERECHTHEION

Caryatid

Tiered seating

Seats for 14,000 people

Orchestra

Stage building

OPEN-AIR THEATRE
The Greeks built large open-air theatres. This print shows the theatre at Epidauros, which dates from about 350 B.C. Its tiered (sloped) stone seating was arranged in a semicircle in front of the stage building. No one knows how this building looked, as only the foundations remain. The circular orchestra was a space for dancing.

PARTHENON

This temple of the Greek goddess Athena dominates the Acropolis. It is an example of the Doric order built between 447 and 432 B.C. The columns have plain capitals. They support a pediment (triangular part of wall above the entablature) that was once adorned with marble sculptures.

A band of sculpture, called a frieze, once ran behind the colonnade where it was protected.

Fluted (vertically channelled) marble columns of the Doric order

Remains of pediment

ANCIENT ROME

THE ROMANS' HUGE EMPIRE stretched from Britain to Asia and Africa. They adapted the classical style of the Greeks, adding domes, vaults, arches, and brickwork, and used concrete for the first time.

Everyday buildings

While most citizens lived in compact town houses built around courtyards, the rich also had large country houses or villas. Many of these houses were ornate and impressive. Some villas had a form of central heating called a hypocaust. Hot air from a fire flowed beneath the floors.

Small courtyards

Main courtyard

The audience chamber dominated the whole complex.

FISHBOURNE VILLA
This villa in England belonged to a local king who became a Roman citizen. The house was decorated with marble from Italy, mosaic pavements, and wall paintings. The rooms were arranged around a large courtyard.

TRAJAN'S MARKETS

An enormous brick-built block of shops and offices, these markets were built by the emperor Trajan in the early 2nd century A.D. The complex included a market hall with shops arranged in a semicircle. Everything from fabrics to spices was sold here.

FACTS AND FIGURES

- The Romans were the first to build multi-storey blocks of flats.

- The Roman city of Pompeii was preserved in ash after Mount Vesuvius erupted in A.D. 79.

- Ancient graffiti has been found on the walls of some of the Romans' buildings.

ARCHWAYS

Arched entrances to the shops were set in a semicircle. An upper level housed small shops.

Main market hall with 12 shops

Street lined with inns and shops

TRAJAN'S MARKETS, ROME

Upper corridor with shops

Terrace

Staircase

Public buildings

With a large empire, the Romans had the labour force and resources to construct huge public buildings. These included temples, markets, basilicas (where courts were held and business conducted), and places of entertainment. Such large buildings showed the power and status of the emperors.

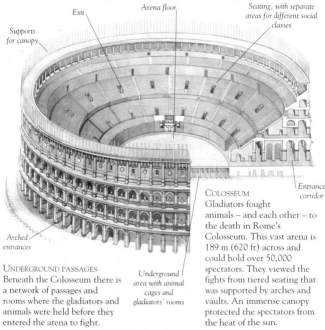

Exit

Arena floor

Seating, with separate areas for different social classes

Supports for canopy

Entrance corridor

Arched entrances

UNDERGROUND PASSAGES
Beneath the Colosseum there is a network of passages and rooms where the gladiators and animals were held before they entered the arena to fight.

Underground area with animal cages and gladiators' rooms

COLOSSEUM
Gladiators fought animals – and each other – to the death in Rome's Colosseum. This vast arena is 189 m (620 ft) across and could hold over 50,000 spectators. They viewed the fights from tiered seating that was supported by arches and vaults. An immense canopy protected the spectators from the heat of the sun.

Window   Coffered vault

Main entrance

Nave

Load-bearing pier with Corinthian column

BASILICA OF CONSTANTINE

Emperor Maxentius (A.D. 306-12) began this building, but it was finished by Constantine I (A.D. 306-37) in A.D. 313. Massive stone piers (supports) carried the weight of the vaulted roof to the floor. This type of structure influenced many later buildings.

RUINS OF BASILICA

The three massive barrel vaults of Rome's Basilica of Constantine are still standing.

PANTHEON

This circular temple in Rome is built of concrete faced with bricks outside and marble inside. It has a large domed roof with a central unglazed oculus (window) to let in sunlight. The coffers (hollow panels) act as decoration and as a way of making the structure lighter.

Portico (colonnaded entrance)

Corinthian column

Unglazed eye

Stepped side of coffer

Coffer

MODEL OF THE INTERIOR OF THE PANTHEON

Marble veneer

EARLY CHRISTIANITY

CONSTANTINE was the first Roman emperor to adopt Christianity in the 4th century. Early Christians adapted the Roman aisled basilica for their first churches. The resulting style of architecture became common in the eastern or Byzantine Empire, and is often known as the Byzantine style.

BYZANTINE CAPITALS
The Byzantines evolved their own style of decoration. Some Byzantine capitals are like the Greek Corinthian type. Others have openwork or finely carved basketwork designs.

CUBICAL   COMPOSITE   CORINTHIAN

SANTA SABINA FACADE

High windows

SANTA SABINA INTERIOR

FACTS AND FIGURES

• Many Byzantine churches are decorated with beautiful mosaics.

• The dome of Hagia Sophia measures 32.6 m (107 ft) across.

• Riots in A.D. 532 led to the destruction of many buildings in Constantinople.

• Byzantine cities had defensive walls up to 12 m (40 ft) high.

SANTA SABINA
This basilica-type church was built on the Aventine hill in Rome in the 5th century. Its nave is flanked by arches with Corinthian columns. A curved sanctuary houses the high altar.

Curved sanctuary

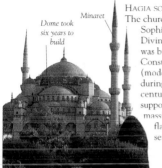

Dome took six years to build

Minaret

HAGIA SOPHIA
The church of Hagia Sophia (the Divine Wisdom) was built in Constantinople (modern Istanbul) during the 6th century. It is supported by massive piers and flanked by two semi-domes.

THE GREAT DOME
Inside the great church the dome, pierced by 40 windows, seems to float above the vast central space, creating a church quite unlike the basilica design.

MINARETS
The dome of Hagia Sophia makes an imposing silhouette. The minarets were added later, when the Muslims conquered the city and turned this church into a mosque.

HAGIA SOPHIA, ISTANBUL

MEDIEVAL BUILDINGS

INTRODUCTION

MANY BUILDINGS OF the medieval age were linked with the rise of organized religion. In the Far East, Hinduism and Buddhism were well established, while Islam was spreading in the Middle East, North Africa, and Spain. In western Europe, great Gothic cathedrals demonstrated the faith of the people and the great power of the Church.

WAT SORASAK,
SUKHOTHAI,
THAILAND

Elephant sculptures surround the base of the stupa.

REIMS
CATHEDRAL,
FRANCE

BUDDHIST STUPA
Buddhism spread throughout India, Southeast Asia, China, and Japan. The typical Buddhist building was the stupa, an earth mound clad in brick or stone. It was often decorated with sacred animal carvings.

CHRISTIAN CATHEDRAL
Christians built Gothic-style cathedrals all over Western Europe. Armies of labourers, with specialized workers, such as stonemasons, glassmakers, and carpenters, often took decades to build them.

AL AZHAR MOSQUE, CAIRO, EGYPT

Minaret

Dome

ISLAMIC MOSQUE
As the Muslims conquered new peoples, Islamic builders took the traditional mosque design farther afield. There was usually a domed prayer hall, a courtyard, and at least one minaret.

PYRAMID OF THE GIANT JAGUAR, TIKAL, GUATEMALA

Carved stone altars

Stairway

Entrance to the temple chamber

AZTEC CALENDAR STONE
The Aztecs were skilled builders and scientists. They represented their calendar on stones like the one above.

MAYAN PYRAMID
The peoples of Central America, such as the Maya, continued to build temples on top of tall pyramids. Many temples were shaped to amplify the voices of the priests, so that people at ground level could follow the ceremonies.

MEDIEVAL VERNACULAR

IN MEDIEVAL EUROPE, everyday buildings were built with whatever materials were available. Builders used a simple style that was influenced by the local materials and climate rather than the latest architectural fashion. As a result, these structures – known as vernacular buildings – were built in the same style for hundreds of years.

Cruck frame

WATTLE AND DAUB
Many walls in this period were made of wattle (wooden strips) and daub (a mixture of clay and dung).

CRUCK-FRAMED HOUSE
An early type of frame building was the cruck frame. The main beams made an upside-down V-shape, visible at both ends of the building. The space between was filled with wattle and daub.

SECTION OF LONDON BRIDGE, ENGLAND

Stone chapel of St. Thomas

Timber frame

Iron railing

Turret

MODEL OF THE
TOWER OF LONDON,
AFTER 1070

Stone walls

TOWER OF LONDON

Around every castle tower was a group of smaller buildings which served as extra living space, workshops, and stables. These buildings are around the Tower of London in England. Some are cruck-framed buildings; others are straight-sided. The roofs were thatched or covered with tiles or slates depending on the materials available at the time.

Tiled
roof

Wooden fence

Cruck frame

Straight-sided buildings
were popular in the
later medieval period.

LONDON BRIDGE

Medieval bridges, like old London Bridge (demolished in the 17th century), often contained shops and houses. The bridge itself was built in 1209, but the houses and shops were added later in a variety of materials and styles. London Bridge had stone buildings, timber-framed houses in the familiar "black-and-white" style, and other timber-framed buildings faced with plaster or wooden panelling.

House covered with
weatherboarding
(wooden panelling)

Wooden supports hold
up buildings projecting
out over the river.

Stone arch

FACTS AND FIGURES

• Early medieval houses often had only two rooms – one for people, the other for animals.

• There were no chimneys in medieval houses, just a hole in the roof. Heat came from a central fire.

• In 1666, most of London's closely huddled wooden houses burned down in the Great Fire.

CASTLES

THE NOBILITY OF medieval Europe often lived in castles, which were military strongholds as well as homes. A castle was designed to withstand a siege. It was self-sufficient, with workshops, kitchens, stables, and stores. There was also a strong building, called a great tower, or keep.

Castle defence

Builders developed different ways of protecting their buildings from attack. These ranged from earthworks to strong stone towers and rings of stone curtain walls.

Motte

Bailey

ROCHESTER CASTLE, ENGLAND

Keep

MOTTE AND BAILEY
French warriors, known as the Normans, put up many wooden castles. They built a motte (earth mound) with a wooden tower. The bailey (adjoining courtyard) contained wooden huts for people and animals.

STONE CASTLE
In the 11th century, castles often had square keeps with thick walls. A keep held rooms for the lord and his household, a chapel, and storerooms.

Inner ring

PLAN OF KRAK DES CHEVALIERS

Narrow main entrance

Outer ring

CONCENTRIC CASTLE
Some of the strongest castles were built by the crusaders in the Middle East. Krak des Chevaliers in Syria, built in the 12th and 13th centuries, was protected by concentric rings of stone walls. The narrow entrance was easy to defend.

CASTLE ON THE RIVER
There are many castles on the Rhine River, Germany. They are built of local stone, often on high crags. There is usually a tall watchtower for a good view. The other castle buildings are grouped around a courtyard.

The watchtower gives good views over the Rhine River.

MARKSBURG, GERMANY

KNIGHT
Medieval castles were usually the homes of knights who held their castles in return for service to the king. This knight's armour dates from the 15th century.

Inside a castle

Take away one wall of a stone castle keep and you will see the main room where the lord and his family lived. This room was used for both sleeping and eating. Below this were storerooms, and above might be quarters for soldiers. Within the walls were additional small rooms, some of them containing simple lavatories called garderobes.

Battlements

Turret

Fireplace

Hall

Vaulted room

Main entrance

STONE KEEP
This model shows inside the stone keep of the 12th-century castle at Provins, France. The keep contains one hall, or main living room, with staircases and smaller rooms in the turrets. A heavy door, and perhaps a portcullis, would have protected the entrance to the keep.

Embrasure

Staircase

LOOPHOLES

Defenders fired through loopholes set in an embrasure (alcove). Arched openings were set at low levels. Cross-shaped holes were for arrows, circular holes for guns.

ARCHED   CROSS   CIRCULAR

DUNGEONS

Few castles served as prisons, and rooms now called "dungeons" were often simply storerooms. But when people were locked up in a castle, stout oak bars and thick stone walls ensured security.

GATEHOUSE, CAERPHILLY CASTLE, WALES

Machicolations

Loophole

Portcullis

CASTLE GATEHOUSE

The gatehouse was usually well defended. Protected by oak doors and a portcullis, defenders dropped missiles on enemies below through openings called machicolations.

Motte

Staircase

Courtyard

COURTYARD

Castle buildings were often grouped around a central courtyard. An open staircase rises beside the courtyard of this castle at Saumur in France.

ROMANESQUE

THE GRAND BUILDINGS of Western Europe in the early medieval period often imitated Roman architecture. Called Romanesque, this style used round arches, simple vaults, and in some places, Corinthian capitals. Churches were often built to the Romans' basilica design. New features, such as façades with rows of arches and frontages with twin towers, were added.

Decorative arcading

LEANING TOWER OF PISA
This famous leaning tower was built as the bell tower for Pisa Cathedral in Italy. It is circled with decorative arches, called arcading, and leans about 5 m (16.4 ft) to one side.

PISA CATHEDRAL, ITALY

The front of this structure is faced with red and white marble.

Round-headed arches

Tympanum

PISA CATHEDRAL
The west front of Pisa Cathedral uses rounded arches similar to those on the tower. Larger arches surround the doors, each with a decorated semicircular tympanum above them.

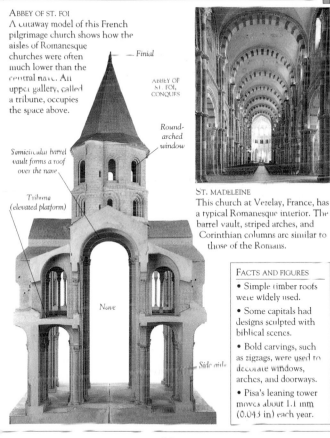

ABBEY OF ST. FOI

A cutaway model of this French pilgrimage church shows how the aisles of Romanesque churches were often much lower than the central nave. An upper gallery, called a tribune, occupies the space above.

Finial

ABBEY OF ST. FOI, CONQUES

Round-arched window

Semicircular barrel vault forms a roof over the nave

Tribune (elevated platform)

Nave

Side aisle

ST. MADELEINE

This church at Vézelay, France, has a typical Romanesque interior. The barrel vault, striped arches, and Corinthian columns are similar to those of the Romans.

FACTS AND FIGURES

- Simple timber roofs were widely used.

- Some capitals had designs sculpted with biblical scenes.

- Bold carvings, such as zigzags, were used to decorate windows, arches, and doorways.

- Pisa's leaning tower moves about 1.1 mm (0.043 in) each year.

GOTHIC

THE 12TH CENTURY saw the emergence of the distinctive Gothic style. Features are pointed arches, large windows, stone tracery, stone vaulted ceilings, and flying buttresses. Many of Europe's finest churches are in this imposing yet delicate style.

CARVING BALLFLOWERS

Ballflowers are typical of 14th-century Gothic. Masons carved these in the sequence shown below. They may have a three- or four-leafed pattern.

LIMESTONE BLOCK

INITIAL CARVING

FINISHED BALLFLOWERS

FACTS AND FIGURES

• Gothic stained glass windows told Bible stories to those who could not read.

• In 1573, the 150-m (500-ft) spire of Beauvais Cathedral, Paris collapsed.

• Spires were built using scaffolding and wooden cranes.

• Notre Dame in Paris was built over a period of 170 years.

Spire

MODEL OF SALISBURY CATHEDRAL FROM THE WEST

Tower

Stone tracery

SALISBURY CATHEDRAL

This English cathedral was built in the 13th century, although the tower and spire were added later. It has simple lancet (a sharp, pointed arch) windows typical of early Gothic. The west front is decorated with blind (filled-in) arcading.

Blind arcading

Triple lancet window

Stained glass window

West doorway

CHURCH OF SAINTE CHAPELLE
This church was built in Paris in the 13th century. It was built for the French royal family, and has the elaborate carved tracery typical of this later period. The apsidal (semicircular) east end of the church is a common feature of French Gothic buildings.

Gothic-style spire added in the 19th century

Interior decorated with blind arcading and statues of the apostles

Pinnacle

UPPER CHAPEL
The 16 windows of the upper chapel are a pictorial Bible, showing over 1,000 scenes from the Old and New Testaments.

Rose Window made up of 86 stained glass panels

MAIN PORTAL
You can clearly see the characteristic Gothic pointed arch in Sainte-Chapelle's main portal, or doorway.

Main portal

Lower chapel

Upper chapel, reserved for the royal family

Notre Dame

Almost 200 years in the making, Notre Dame Cathedral is a landmark not only in Paris, but in Gothic architecture. It has all the characteristic features of the Gothic style. The most striking feature is the elaborate west front with its two imposing towers and rose window. The west front contains the three main entrance doorways and is decorated with rows of statues.

GOTHIC WINDOWS

In the 12th century, Gothic windows were often simple lancets. These were paired in the 13th century to make two-light windows, which can be seen in Notre Dame. Later still, windows were filled with tracery. Two typical tracery styles were geometric and perpendicular.

LANCET   TWO-LIGHT WINDOW   GEOMETRIC TRACERY   PERPENDICULAR TRACERY

INTERIOR

Inside Notre Dame there is a long, tall nave. On either side of the nave are two aisles through which processions marched in medieval times. At the east end of the nave is a sanctuary (holy place) with stalls for the clergy. There are also numerous chapels where small-scale services and masses for the dead were held. A large transept cuts across the nave at right angles to form the shape of a cross when the cathedral is viewed from above.

Notre Dame's towers are 69 m (226 ft) tall.

Gargoyles

West rose window

King's gallery

Main doorway

Notre Dame's spire was added in the 19th century.

Roof of the north transept

South tower

Two-light window

The sanctuary is in the east end of the cathedral

FLYING BUTTRESSES
The huge windows in some Gothic cathedrals meant that the walls were often too weak to support the vaulted ceilings. Architects, therefore, erected flying buttresses to take the strain.

Flying buttress

NOTRE DAME VIEWED FROM THE EAST END

Flying buttresses span 15 m (50 ft)

Ambulatory (passage around the sanctuary)

South rose window

Transept

Stone tracery

Aisle

Nave

Treasury, home of the cathedral's religious artefacts

ISLAMIC ARCHITECTURE

MOSQUES AND TOMBS are usually the most important buildings in Islamic countries. They are decorated with abstract patterns, foliage motifs, and exquisite calligraphy from the Islamic sacred book, the Koran.

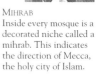

Ceramic tiles

Niche

Middle East and India

The Islamic faith spread rapidly in the 7th century, especially through the Middle East, southern Asia, and northern Africa. A mosque is a building for worship and group prayer. It contains a prayer hall, usually with a domed roof, and may have a courtyard surrounded by arches.

FACTS AND FIGURES

• A mosque is the centre of a Muslim community, and sometimes contains a school in its plan.

• Enclosed courtyards are an important feature of mosques and other Islamic buildings.

• "Stalactites", columns that hang from the ceiling, are used in many Islamic buildings.

Minaret

Dome

BLUE MOSQUE, CAIRO

MIHRAB
Inside every mosque is a decorated niche called a mihrab. This indicates the direction of Mecca, the holy city of Islam.

BLUE MOSQUE
This mosque's large domed prayer hall and tall minaret are typical Islamic features. The minaret is used by a muezzin (an official) to call the faithful to prayer.

TAJ MAHAL
The marble walls of the Taj Mahal are delicately carved with a floral motif and inlaid with semi-precious stones.

PLAN OF THE TAJ MAHAL

1. ROYAL TOMB 4. RESTHOUSE
2. PONDS   5. CANAL
3. MOSQUE   6. GREAT GATEWAY

Minaret

PARADISE ON EARTH
This beautifully symmetrical building at Agra, India, is decorated with inscriptions from the Koran. The Mogul emperor, Shah Jehan, built it in the 17th century as a tomb for his wife Mumtaz Mahal.

Dome of marble

Plinth to raise the tomb above ground level

TAJ MAHAL, AGRA, INDIA

Islamic Spain

Spain was ruled by Muslims for several centuries during the medieval period. Known as the Moors, these people came from Syria and northern Africa, and their style of architecture was influenced by these areas. Their mosques and palaces have shady courtyards, forests of pillars, scalloped arches, and ornate, plaster ceiling decorations.

One of 24 fortified towers

Hall of the Two Sisters

Scalloped arch

Ornate "stalactite" plasterwork

Horseshoe arch

Colonnade

GREAT MOSQUE
This mosque at Cordoba in Spain was begun in A.D.785. Its arches have alternating bands of brick and stone, giving a striped effect. The original arches were round, but horseshoe and scalloped arches followed.

ALHAMBRA

This palace-fortress was the last stronghold of the Moors in Granada, southern Spain. Inside its strong outer walls, colonnaded courtyards with fountains and covered walks offer shade from the hot sun. The luxurious rooms are richly decorated with stone carvings, mosaic tiles and ornate plasterwork.

FORTIFIED PALACE

The Alhambra is positioned on the top of a hill and protected by its high red brick walls. It was built between 1238 and 1358 by Moorish princes.

There were more than 100 columns in the Court of the Lions.

Court of the Lions is named after the 12 stone lions at the base of the fountain.

Lion fountain

Hall of Abencerrajes

INDIA

INDIA IS HOME TO A HOST of different cultures and religious influences, and has a diversity of building styles and techniques. Hinduism, with its many gods, and Buddhism, with its emphasis on the individual's search for enlightenment, have produced a variety of religious buildings. These range from domed-shaped Buddhist shrines (or stupas) to Jain and Hindu temples with pointed roofs.

ELLURA TEMPLE OF ROCK
This Hindu temple is carved out of solid rock. From outside, the natural face of the cliff can be seen above the carvings of elephants and round pillars.

Carved pillar

INSIDE ELLURA
Inside the Ellura temples, forests of pillars, carved roofs, and entire statues have been hewn out of the cliff. In some places the rock has been cut through to allow sunlight in.

DILWARRA JAIN TEMPLE

This sumptuous shrine at Mount Abu was built in the 10th century. The interior is of marble, which had to be brought to the site along a specially made sloping roadway. The roof is a shallow, intricately carved dome supported on pillars.

GREAT STUPA, SANCHI

The four gates symbolize the winds

Dome

GREAT STUPA

This building was originally at the heart of a Buddhist monastery. It is based on an earth mound. The original bricks on the outside were replaced by stone in *c.*150 B.C.

KHANDARIYA MAHADEVA TEMPLE, INDIA

Ritual carvings

Conical tower

MOUNTAIN OF STONE

The huge, conical tower of this and similar Hindu temples has been compared to huge mountains of stone. In fact, they are intended to imitate the mythical Mount Meru, which is supposed to separate heaven and Earth.

SOUTHEAST ASIA

TWO EARLY CIVILIZATIONS of Southeast Asia, the Sailendra of Java and the Khmers of Cambodia, have left impressive evidence of their architecture, dating from the 9th to 13th centuries. In Cambodia, Hindu temple-cities were built to glorify the god-kings of the Khmer empire. The Buddhist stupas (shrines) of Java, by contrast, are designed to encourage meditation.

BOROBUDUR,
JAVA,
INDONESIA

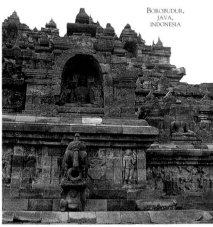

BOROBUDUR
This 9th century Javanese stupa is built with grey volcanic stone. Statues of Buddha are present to encourage people to follow his path toward enlightenment.

STONE TERRACES
This building is a great mound with nine stone terraces. The lower terraces are decorated with relief carvings of the life of Buddha; the upper storeys are plainer.

GUARDIAN OF
ANGKOR WAT
Gate-guards like this one
are set on the tall towers
of this 12th-century
temple in Cambodia.
The Khmers believed the
guards protected the
shrine. The walls of the
gallery are decorated
with carved reliefs.

TEMPLE CITY
The Khmer kings built vast
sandstone temples to be buried in.
This temple at Angkor (the
capital of the Khmer civilization)
is built around courtyards and
surrounded by
moats. It is
famous for its
tall, conical
towers.

Conical sandstone
tower

Gallery
richly
decorated
with reliefs

Portico

ANGKOR WAT,
CAMBODIA

EARLY AMERICAN CIVILIZATIONS

SOME EARLY AMERICAN buildings still remain today. The Maya flourished in Central America between A.D. 200 and 1000; the Aztecs in Mexico in the 14th to 16th centuries; and the Incas in Peru in the 15th and 16th centuries.

The Maya

The Maya were based in cities around Mexico, Honduras, and Guatemala. Their most impressive buildings were pyramids consisting of stone-clad earth mounds with terracing, steps up the side, and stone temples on top.

LOCATION OF THE MAYA
The Maya kingdom occupied much of central America.

Inner core

Outer facing of stone

The pyramid consisted of nine steep stone steps.

People could stand on each level.

TEMPLE OF THE INSCRIPTIONS

This pyramid at Palenque in Mexico was built in the 7th century, and consists of a stepped mound of earth, faced with stone. Inside the pyramid is the tomb of the Mayan king Pacal. The temple on top of the pyramid has carved panels describing the events of the king's reign.

TEMPLE

CENTRAL PLAZA

The Temple of the Inscriptions stands in what was Palenque's central plaza, near the palace and other temples. Today, only this central area is visible. The other parts of the city are covered by dense rainforest.

Temple

Steps to tomb (blocked after the king's burial)

Outer steps to temple

King's tomb

SECTION PULLED OUT FROM MAIN ARTWORK

Memorial slab

FACTS AND FIGURES

• The Pyramid of the Sun at Teotihuacan is just over 60 m (200 ft) tall.

• Mayan pyramids were decorated with coloured plaster.

• Some Mayan cities, such as Tikal, had populations of 40,000 to 50,000.

• Most Mayan pyramids are simple platforms for temples.

The Aztecs

For over a century, the Aztec people held power over Mexico. They built a large city called Tenochtitlán where Mexico City now stands. In the middle of the city was a walled compound which was the centre of Aztec religion. The Aztecs practised human sacrifice, believing that it pleased their gods. Their pyramidal temples were similar to those of the Mayan people.

ATLANTIC OCEAN

The Aztecs

PACIFIC OCEAN

LOCATION OF THE AZTECS
From the city of Tenochtitlán, the Aztecs gradually expanded throughout Mexico.

STONE DEITIES
The Aztecs had many gods and goddesses. Here, stone carvings of these deities peer from the top of the temple.

Victims were thrown down these steps after being sacrificed.

Snake's head protruding from wall

Shrine to Tlaloc

Shrine to Huitzilopochtli

Sacrificial stone

c.1431
c.1454
c.1469
c.1390
c.1500

QUETZALCOATL
This image shows the feathered-serpent god, Quetzalcoatl. This was the god of self sacrifice, and inventor of agriculture in Aztec myths.

The remains of five separate temples have been found on the same site.

GREAT TEMPLE AT TENOCHTITLAN
On top of this enormous stone pyramid stood twin shrines dedicated to Tlaloc, the god of rain, and Huitzilopochtli, the god of war. Beneath the outer stone "skin" of the pyramid, archaeologists have found a succession of smaller temples, covered as each new Aztec ruler built a bigger temple on the same site.

Outer stone covering

The Incas

South America's first great builders were the Incas, who established a large empire in the west of the continent during the 15th century. Their buildings were made of irregularly shaped stones which skilled stonemasons ground to fit together perfectly. These stone buildings still exist in their best-preserved city, Machu Picchu in Peru, and at the Inca capital of Cuzco.

ATLANTIC
OCEAN

The Inca

PACIFIC
OCEAN

LOCATION OF THE INCAS
The Inca Empire spread along the west coast of what is now Peru, and parts of Bolivia and Chile.

MACHU
PICCHU,
PERU

Farming
terraces

Central
plaza

MACHU PICCHU
Perched some 3,150 m (9,000 ft) above sea level, the ancient city of Machu Picchu is a stunning example of Inca building. The stone blocks of the stairs linking its different levels were cut so precisely that no mortar was required.

FORTRESS OF SACSAHUAMAN

This large fortress overlooks the city of Cuzco. It is built of massive stone blocks – some as big as 8.2 m (27 ft) high – which make up thick, zigzagging walls. The 0.5-km (0.3-mile) long building provided a secure refuge for the inhabitants of the Inca capital in troubled times.

GATE OF THE SUN

Evidence of the high degree of skill attained by early South American stonemasons is borne by this gateway at the city of Tiahuanaco. Almost one thousand years old, it is cut from a single block of stone 3 m (10 ft) high. The carved head is probably a portrait of an Inca god.

Carved head

Houses   *Stone staircase*

TERRACED CITY

With its Temple of the Sun, palace, buildings of local stone, and terraces for crop growing, Machu Picchu is typical of an Inca provincial city. The buildings vary in shape, but most have trapezoid (tapering) windows and doorways.

THE EUROPEAN RENAISSANCE

INTRODUCTION

ARCHITECTS IN 15TH-CENTURY Italy were the first to be influenced by the Renaissance, the intellectual movement that revived the learning and artistic styles of classical Greece and Rome. The influence of Italian Renaissance architecture, with its emphasis on symmetry and space, spread throughout Europe, ending in the extravagant decoration of early 18th-century baroque.

ITALIAN PALACE
Renaissance princes often lived in elegant classical palaces, decorated with details inspired by the buildings of ancient Greece and Rome. This one, the Palazzo del Te, was built by Giulio Romano in Mantua.

SCULPTORS' FRIEZE
In the Renaissance period, classical styles were revived in all the arts, not just architecture. Some architects, such as Bernini and Michelangelo, were also sculptors. Renaissance buildings were often adorned with elegant statues.

CHATEAU DE
CHENONCEAUX, FRANCE

FACTS AND FIGURES

• *Renaissance* is a French word which means rebirth.

• Pierre Lescot (c.1686-1746) was an influential architect of the French Renaissance.

• The proportions of the human body were considered ideal, and were imitated in Renaissance buildings

FRENCH CHATEAU

While the Italians were building grand, classical palaces, the French built many less formally designed châteaux, some of which include fascinating features. This château at Chenonceaux is built partly on an arched bridge over the River Cher.

The deep cut edges of the stone produce an effect called rustication.

Doric pilasters (half columns)

IDEAL CITY

Italian Renaissance architects were fascinated by the concept of the ideal city, planned from scratch with beautiful vistas and imposing public buildings. This plan for a city dates from 1552. Its circular design was thought to be the perfect shape.

ITALIAN RENAISSANCE

RENAISSANCE architecture first appeared in the great Italian cities of Milan, Florence, Rome, and Venice. This new style of building based on the architecture of ancient Greece and Rome replaced the pointed-arched Gothic style with domed roofs and classical columns.

Central domed great hall rises the entire height of the villa

VILLA CAPRA

This country house in Vicenza, also known as the Rotonda, was begun by Italian architect Andrea Palladio in 1552. Its plan is a perfect square, and the entrance portico is flanked by tall Ionic columns.

FACTS AND FIGURES

• Florence was the first Italian city to reflect the influence of the Renaissance in its architecture.

• Italian Filippo Brunelleschi (1377-1446) was a very influential architect of the time.

• Michelangelo designed the dome of St. Peter's in Rome. It is 135 m (452 ft) high.

PALAZZO PANDOLFINI

Italian painter and architect Raphael designed this palace in Florence in the early 16th century. The decoration is typical of its time. The windows have columns on either side and ornamental pediments.

Pediment

Rustication

Coloured marble

SANTA MARIA NOVELLA

Architect Leon Battista Alberti added an ornate west façade to this medieval church in Florence in 1456-70. It features a triangular pediment, Corinthian columns, and coloured marble patterns.

THE TEMPIETTO, ROME

The Tempietto marks the spot where St. Peter is thought to have died.

Dome in shape of hemisphere

Doric column

DOORWAYS

Italian Renaissance doorways are often highly decorated and topped with a triangular pediment. Many have classical columns and carved stonework.

DOORWAY BY VIGNOLA

DOORWAY BY CARDI

DOORWAY BY SERLIO

DOMED CHAPEL

The Tempietto was built by Donato Bramante in 1502-10. It is modelled on a small round classical temple, with a dome and a ring of 16 Doric columns. The interior of this compact building is 4.5 m (15 ft) in diameter. It stands in the courtyard of San Pietro in Montorio, Rome.

Crypt

FRENCH RENAISSANCE

THE RENAISSANCE CAME later to France than it did to Italy. The first French Renaissance buildings were designed in the 16th century, and often show a combination of Gothic and classical details. Square-headed windows, steeply sloping roofs, and a restrained use of ornament are the trademarks of the style.

FRENCH WINDOWS
These were often square-headed, with swags (carvings of foliage or looped draperies). Curved-headed windows followed later.

EARLY WINDOW   MIDDLE WINDOW   LATE WINDOW

Slim bell tower is typical of the Renaissance

ST. ETIENNE DU MONT, PARIS

Carved pediment

Rood screen with double spiral staircases

Rose window

PARISIAN CHURCH
French Renaissance buildings often show a mixture of styles. This church in Paris has a rose window, like those in some Gothic churches, and a delicate rood screen (the balcony holding the crucifix). The carved pediment is a typical Renaissance feature.

PALACE OF VERSAILLES

This enormous palace outside Paris was built for King Louis XIV by the architects Louis Le Vau and Jules Hardouin-Mansart. It is one of the biggest palaces ever built. Construction, which began in 1660, took almost 100 years. The staterooms and apartments are big enough to accommodate thousands of people.

The park façade was built between 1678-88

CHATEAU DE CHAMBORD, LOIRE

CHAPELLE ROYALE

The interior of this chapel at Versailles is richly decorated with white marble, gilding, and baroque murals. The top floor was reserved to be used only by the royal family.

Large windows

PALACE FORTRESS

In the early Renaissance period, French monarchs and nobles still built castles. Château de Chambord was built for King François I in the 16th century. It is based on the medieval plan, with a keep and four towers, but is covered in Renaissance decoration. This decoration makes it look more like a palace than a fortress.

ENGLAND, HOLLAND, AND BELGIUM

LOCAL TRADITIONS influenced the Renaissance architecture of England, Holland, and Belgium. Quite unlike the style of Italy, buildings have large windows, ornate facades, and rich details, both inside and out. A stronger use of classical details, however, emerged during the 17th century.

ENGLAND
The English nobles of the late 16th century built a series of large country houses. Burghley in Northamptonshire is one of the grandest, with its dome-topped corner towers and gatehouse.

BURGHLEY HOUSE, ENGLAND

HARDWICK HALL
This Great Chamber is a superb example of a late 16th-century English interior. Its large windows, plaster friezes, tapestries, and wood panelling are all original.

Turreted entrance

Corner tower

ANTWERP TOWN HALL, BELGIUM

Classical details are used freely on the central tower.

Open gallery

Projecting eaves

MAURITSHUIS, THE HAGUE, HOLLAND

Relief sculpture

Dutch steep roof

BELGIUM

Antwerp town hall is a typical early Renaissance building. It was designed by Cornelis Floris in 1561-66. Neat rows of windows give a regimented appearance, except for the elaborate tower in the centre.

FACTS AND FIGURES

- Inigo Jones (1573-1652) brought the classical influence to English architecture.
- Lieven de Kay (1560-1627) and Hendrik de Keyser (1565-1621) created the Dutch style.
- Cornelius Floris (1504-75) was influential in Belgium.

HOLLAND

This grand house in The Hague was built in c.1633. With its tall Ionic columns rising the full height of two storeys, and its triangular pediments over the doors and windows, it is a good example of the Dutch style of the mid-17th century.

BAROQUE

DURING THE 17TH CENTURY, a style emerged based on curved forms, rich materials, complex shapes, and dramatic lighting. It came to be called baroque, which originally meant irregular or misshapen. The first baroque buildings were seen in Italy, but the style spread to many other parts of Europe.

Italian baroque

The beginnings of baroque were in Rome, where architects Bernini and Borromini worked. Bernini began his career as a sculptor, and elements of his training can be seen in the baroque style. Statues are used as supports, and the curved walls appear to be moulded.

FACTS AND FIGURES

• Paintings are used to create false perspectives in Melk Abbey, Austria.

• In Rome, baroque became an expression of the power of the Catholic church.

• Baroque was based on the traditional classical style, but added new features.

DOME OF SAN CARLO ALLE QUATTRO FONTANE
This church in Rome was designed by Borromini. Its interior is dominated by a beautiful dome, which is coffered (recessed) using a variety of different shapes. It is lit by windows that are concealed from view and highlight the shapes in the dome.

BAROQUE DETAILS

Italian baroque buildings often have rich sculptural details. Niches, altarpieces, and façades are all common places for such statues.

ECSTASY OF ST. TERESA BY BERNINI

BUTTRESS WITH STATUE

SANTA SUSANNA, ROME

Pediment

Scrolled buttress

Statue in niche

Pilaster

SAN ANDREA AL QUIRINALE

Pink marble covers the interior walls of this church in Rome. It was designed by Bernini, demonstrating the liking of baroque architects for rich materials. Sculptures around the dome reach up to the central lantern, pointing towards the heavens.

ORNATE FAÇADE

The scrolled brackets and the statues in niches mark Santa Susanna's façade as baroque. The spaces between the pilasters (half-columns) are varied, unlike the earlier Renaissance style which mostly used equally spaced rows of columns.

Northern baroque

The baroque style spread to northern Europe
in the early 18th century. In England the result
was a more severe, solid-looking style, with
fewer curves but much of the rich detail found
in European baroque. In Austria and Germany,
interiors of great extravagance were produced,
with lavish use of gilding and false-perspective
ceiling paintings.

ST. GEORGE-IN-THE-EAST
Nicholas Hawksmoor designed several baroque
churches in London. They are solid-looking
buildings with heavy cornices, prominent
triangular pediments, and striking steeples. Four
pepper-pot lanterns add delicacy to this example.

ST. GEORGE-
IN-THE-EAST,
LONDON

Steeple

Cornice

Pediment

BLENHEIM PALACE,
OXFORDSHIRE,
ENGLAND

*Side
wings*

*Classical columns
of the entrance
portico*

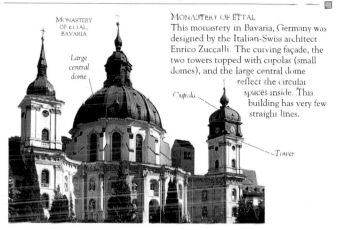

MONASTERY OF ETTAL, BAVARIA

Large central dome

Cupola

Tower

MONASTERY OF ETTAL
This monastery in Bavaria, Germany was designed by the Italian-Swiss architect Enrico Zuccalli. The curving façade, the two towers topped with cupolas (small domes), and the large central dome reflect the circular spaces inside. This building has very few straight lines.

BENEDICTINE MONASTERY
Most of the inside surfaces of this baroque church in Melk, Austria are decorated lavishly, from the bases of the fluted columns to the ceiling frescoes.

BLENHEIM PALACE
This Oxfordshire country house, designed by Sir John Vanbrugh, was a gift to the Duke of Marlborough. With its lofty rooms, four ornamented corner towers, and grand classical columns, it was built as a showpiece.

CHURCH WITHIN MONASTERY, MELK, AUSTRIA

TOWN PLANNING
IN THE 18TH CENTURY

WHOLE NEW CITY DISTRICTS, or sometimes entire cities, were built from scratch in the 18th century. The reasons why this could happen varied. The Russian imperial city of St. Petersburg was created by Peter the Great as the new capital on the banks of the Neva River. The elegant streets of Bath were built to provide a holiday resort for the rich of England.

AERIAL VIEW OF BATH
John Wood I designed the Circus, a circular street of 33 houses. In each house, Doric, Ionic, and Corinthian orders are used for the ground, first and second floors respectively. His son, John Wood II, designed the nearby Royal Crescent and Assembly Rooms.

Royal Crescent   The Circus   Assembly Rooms

ROYAL CRESCENT,
BATH, ENGLAND

*Ionic
column*

ROYAL CRESCENT

The Royal Crescent in Bath is a great sweeping arc of 30 houses that stands on the crest of a hill. Ionic columns are doubled up at either end and in the centre of the crescent, to give extra weight.

*Balustraded
parapet*

Entablature

ST. PETERSBURG

This Russian city was founded in 1703 by Tsar Peter the Great. He employed architects from Italy to create a lavish plan on the banks of the River Neva, with broad avenues radiating out from the central Admiralty and Winter Palace buildings. The south bank contains the historical centre of the city; on the north are museums and a university.

CENTRAL
ST. PETERSBURG

Admiralty

*Winter
Palace*

THE INDUSTRIAL AGE

INTRODUCTION

INNOVATIONS IN THE production of iron and steel, and the manufacture of textiles during the 18th century, forced many countries to move from an agricultural to an industrial economy. There was a need for different types of buildings. More people lived in cities, so large numbers of houses had to be built for them. Factories, too, were needed to house the new machinery for the manufacturing industries.

WATT'S STEAM ENGINE

STEAM ENGINE

The steam engine was a major driving force behind the Industrial Revolution, providing essential power to drive machinery. It was manufactured by Scottish engineer James Watt.

IRON BRIDGE

Iron is a highly adaptable material, allowing new types of structures, such as the first iron bridge, to be built. The bridge has a 30-m (100-ft) span over the River Severn in England. A new town, called Ironbridge, grew up around it.

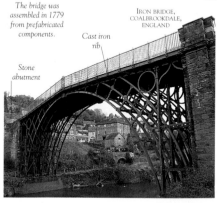

The bridge was assembled in 1779 from prefabricated components.

IRON BRIDGE, COALBROOKDALE, ENGLAND

Cast iron rib

Stone abutment

WORKERS' HOUSING

As industrialization spread, more and more people moved to the cities. They lived in small houses and went to work in the new factories. In England, the workers lived in long, straight streets of compact terraced houses.

RAILWAY WORKERS' COTTAGES, WILTSHIRE, ENGLAND

BLISS MILL, OXFORDSHIRE, ENGLAND

Built in 1872, this mill has the characteristic tall chimney.

Rows of windows provide optimum light

PLACE OF WORK

The 18th and 19th centuries were great eras of factory building. Inside, wide floors, often supported by iron columns, housed the machinery connected by drive belts to a steam engine. The outer walls were of brick, and many had a tall chimney.

FACTS AND FIGURES

- The first steam-powered loom appeared in 1787.
- Gas lighting appeared in *c.*1800.
- New types of buildings, such as warehouses and railway stations, sprang up.
- Built in less than a year, London's Crystal Palace had a staggering 3,300 iron columns

INDUSTRIAL ARCHITECTURE

AS INDUSTRIALIZATION SPREAD, iron became more widely available. Builders recognized that iron made building quicker and easier. If standard-length columns and beams were used, any number could be brought to the site and rapidly bolted together.

Buildings for industry

The rise of industry brought with it a demand for factories to house large machines and hundreds of workers, and for vast warehouses in which goods could be stored. Such buildings required large, uninterrupted floor areas. Brick or stone walls with slim iron columns provided the solution.

Venetian windows

FACTS AND FIGURES

• Iron smelting first began in c.1500 B.C.

• Steel is a modified form of iron with great strength and flexibility.

• The Eiffel Tower is 15 cm (6 in) taller on hot days when the iron structure expands.

• James Watt pioneered the steam engine and metal-framed buildings.

MILL
Industrial buildings of the 18th and 19th centuries often conceal an iron structure inside a skin of brick. The white quoins (corner stones) and the Venetian windows in this English cotton mill recall Renaissance buildings.

Iron tie rod

Brick vault

Iron column

Iron beam

FLAX-SPINNING MILL
This mill in Shrewsbury, England, was built in 1796. It has a skeleton of cast-iron columns, beams, and rods. Iron is also used for the large lattice framed windows. The outside of the building is walled in brick. Each floor has a brick-vaulted ceiling to cut down the risk of fire.

Iron lattice window

SMYTHE BUILDING, PHILADELPHIA, USA

OFFICE BUILDING
In the U.S.A., architects used iron on the outside of buildings. This office building in Philadelphia uses iron and glass to produce an Italian Renaissance effect.

PUMPING STATION
This London pumping station was built in 1865-68. Joseph Bazalgette used ornate iron arches, brackets, and walkways in this "industrial cathedral".

ABBEY MILLS PUMPING STATION, LONDON, ENGLAND

New materials and structures

Spurred on by the need for new buildings, such as large railway stations and exhibition halls, 19th-century architects and engineers began to experiment with new ways of building with iron and steel. They created structures in which the skeleton of steel is the main feature. Steel frameworks could span vast interiors, and enabled very tall buildings to be constructed for the first time. These huge buildings could also be erected at lightning speed.

CRYSTAL PALACE
Built for the Great Exhibition of 1851, Paxton's Crystal Palace was constructed of prefabricated cast iron parts and sheets of glass, in some 22 weeks. After the exhibition, the entire 564-m (1,851-ft) building was taken apart and moved to another site.

LIVERPOOL ST. STATION
Steel has greater tensile strength than iron and is an ideal material for the great arched train sheds that cover the platforms of major railway stations. This station in London was built in 1874-5.

CRYSTAL PALACE, LONDON

The Crystal Fountain

Living elm trees left standing inside

EIFFEL
TOWER,
PARIS

EIFFEL TOWER

When it was built in 1889, the Eiffel Tower was the tallest building in the world: including the antennae, it is now 320 m (1,051 ft) high. Built by engineer Gustave Eiffel as a temporary landmark during the Universal Exhibition, the steel structure has remained a symbol of Paris.

Splayed base and open construction mean the tower hardly sways in the wind.

GALERIE DES
MACHINES,
PARIS

Trussed iron arch

LIFT MECHANISM, EIFFEL TOWER

The original hydraulic lift mechanism still hauls the large, double-decker lift to the top of the Eiffel Tower.

GALERIE DES MACHINES

Vast trussed arches created a huge span 114 m (374 ft) high in the Galerie des Machines, a hall built in Paris for the 1889 exhibition. The two sides of the arches were pinned together at the top, to allow for the expansion of the steel in the heat.

REVIVALISM

IN THE 18TH AND 19TH centuries, architects began to revive ancient styles of architecture. First they looked to ancient Greece and Rome, producing buildings that looked like classical temples. Later they revived the medieval Gothic style.

The classical revival

Interest in ancient Greece increased in the 18th century, resulting in a fashion for buildings in the Greek style which lasted into the 19th century. Buildings often featured imposing porticos (porches) with massive columns.

ALL SOUL'S CHURCH, LANGHAM PLACE
This London church was built by John Nash in 1822-25. The circular portico features Ionic and Corinthian columns.

CAPITOL BUILDING, U.S.A.

CAPITOL BUILDING
This famous structure in Washington, D.C. was rebuilt several times between 1793 and 1867. The huge dome is made mainly of cast iron.

FACTS AND FIGURES

• The dome of the Capitol Building is 30 m (98 ft) wide.

• French architects were influenced by ancient buildings of Rome.

• British architects preferred the style of ancient Greece.

• The spires of Cologne Cathedral (1842-80) are 157 m (515 ft) high.

OPÉRA DE PARIS
Commissioned by Napoleon III in 1862, this is one of the world's largest theatres. As well as a huge auditorium and a vast foyer, there is a staircase with balconies from which fashionable Parisians observed each other.

Copper-green roofed cupola

Grand Foyer

Auditorium

Grand Staircase

PANTHÉON
Inside this famous Paris church, the arms of the building meet at a large central dome.

SHRINE TO THE FAMOUS
King Louis XV commissioned the Panthéon after recovering from an illness. It was finished in 1790, during the French Revolution, and contains the tombs of many famous French people.

Triple layered dome

The carved pediment shows France giving laurel wreaths to her great men.

Portico with Corinthian columns

Crypt containing tombs of famous French men and women

Gothic revival

During the 18th century, there was a reaction against the serious classicism of Greek revival buildings, and some architects began to build in an imitation of medieval Gothic. The first Gothic revival buildings were country houses, which used Gothic motifs with wit and delicacy. But by the 19th century, the Gothic revival had become more solemn – the style was used mostly for churches and cathedrals.

ST. JOHN THE DIVINE, NEW YORK

Position of planned central tower

Pulpit

REVIVAL CATHEDRAL
New York's St. John the Divine was begun in 1892, and is still unfinished. It already boasts many features typical of large medieval churches – pointed arches, flying buttresses, and an ornate west front with a rose window. Twin west towers, and a taller central tower, are planned.

The Rose Window was completed in 1933.

The portals of the West Front are adorned with fine stone carvings.

COUNTRY HOUSE
This 18th-century English house in Gloucestershire has an elegant porch, patterned windows, and plain castle-like battlements.

Pointed arches

Ogee mouldings

LACOCK ABBEY
The elegant great hall of this English country house has windows, with ogee (double-curved) mouldings, and a flower-shaped window typical of 18th-century Gothic revival buildings.

KEBLE COLLEGE, OXFORD
William Butterfield designed this with the chapel, hall, and students' rooms set around a quadrangle. It is constructed in a dazzling striped red, grey, and yellow pattern called polychrome.

ORIENTAL REVIVAL
There was a fashion in 19th-century England for imitating oriental buildings. The Royal Pavilion, Brighton, summer house of the Prince Regent, was designed in a mixture of Chinese and Indian styles by John Nash.

Onion dome

Saloon

Music room

DETAILS OF ROYAL PAVILION, BRIGHTON

MODERN ARCHITECTURE

INTRODUCTION

ARCHITECTS BEGAN TO TURN AWAY from the old styles at the end of the 19th century. They were influenced by the availability of new materials, such as reinforced concrete, and new techniques of construction. A simple, more functional form evolved, and as it spread came to be known as the International Style.

1930S CAR
Increasingly in the 20th century, architects have drawn on fields outside building for their designs. The chrome-plated interiors of some Art Deco buildings were influenced by the sleek, stylish cars of the time – symbols of a new modern era.

FACTS AND FIGURES

• The term "Modern Architecture" caught on after an exhibition in New York in 1932.

• The Dutch De Stijl group was influenced by abstract and cubist art.

• The Louisiana Superdome, U.S.A., has a dome 82 m (273 ft) tall.

• Chicago's Sears Tower, built in 1974, is still the world's tallest building.

HOUSING SCHEME AT KIEFHOOK, HOLLAND

Oud planned every internal detail of these compact houses.

WORKERS' HOUSING
The Dutch architect J.J.P. Oud designed modern housing for ordinary people. These workers' houses, designed in the 1920s, have symmetrical layouts, simple lines, white walls, and minimal ornament typical of early 20th-century buildings.

SCHLUMBERGER RESEARCH INSTITUTE

Architect Michael Hopkins came up with a novel design for this building, which houses offices and laboratories. Steel masts and cables tower above a floor of steel and glass. These support a fabric roof, making the building look like a gigantic tent billowing above the surrounding, flat countryside.

MONTREAL EXPO 67 DOME

American inventor and designer Richard Buckminster Fuller created the geodesic dome as a way of enclosing a large space in a structure with a relatively small surface area. These strong but lightweight domes have proved useful for factories and exhibitions. Materials as diverse as bamboo, plastic, and cardboard can be used to form the framework.

This dome is 60 m (200 ft) high.

U. S. PAVILION AT MONTREAL'S EXPO 67

Interlocking steel struts

Plexiglass panels

THE ROOTS OF MODERN ARCHITECTURE

AT THE TURN of the century, fresh approaches to architecture began to emerge: the strong, simple work of the German Peter Behrens; the elegant buildings of Scotsman Charles Rennie Mackintosh; and the lavish style of the Art Nouveau movement.

A.E.G. TURBINE BUILDING
Peter Behrens designed this Berlin factory in 1908-9. Its curving corners and sloping glass walls make the factory both elegant and functional.

RED HOUSE
This house was built by Philip Webb for designer and writer William Morris in 1859. It mixes Gothic details, such as pointed arches, with later features, like sash windows. This style became known as Arts and Crafts.

RED HOUSE, BEXLEYHEATH, ENGLAND

Gothic-style pointed window

Rectangular sash window

GLASGOW SCHOOL OF ART
This highly original building was designed in 1896 by Charles Rennie Mackintosh. Its entrance shows how Mackintosh combined two different styles: elements of a traditional building are mixed with gentle curves influenced by the Art Nouveau movement.

THE LIBRARY
This is the school's most striking room. There are no curves in its design. Instead, rows of rectangular pillars and beams support the surrounding balcony.

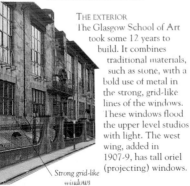

THE EXTERIOR
The Glasgow School of Art took some 12 years to build. It combines traditional materials, such as stone, with a bold use of metal in the strong, grid-like lines of the windows. These windows flood the upper level studios with light. The west wing, added in 1907-9, has tall oriel (projecting) windows.

Strong grid-like windows

FACTS AND FIGURES

• Chairs designed by Mackintosh are still manufactured today.

• The Red House was Philip Webb's first commission.

• Behrens was also a teacher whose pupils included Le Corbusier and Mies van der Rohe.

• Mackintosh's work was more famous in Europe than in Britain.

ART NOUVEAU

WITH ITS FLOWING LINES and curves, the style that became known as Art Nouveau (new art) was created by a group of architects and designers at the end of the 19th century. Art Nouveau flourished briefly in France, Scotland, and Belgium, home of one of its most famous architects, Victor Horta.

Ornate roofs and spires adorned by mosaics

HOUSE IN PARC GUELL, BARCELONA, SPAIN

CASA MILA, AN APARTMENT BUILDING DESIGNED BY GAUDI

ANTONI GAUDI

The Catalan architect Antoni Gaudí designed many buildings in his native Barcelona. His work ranged from houses and apartment buildings to a cathedral and a city park, Parc Guell. Gaudí's buildings are full of curves; in some even the rooms have curved walls. Many are decorated with brilliant mosaics.

PARIS MÉTRO ENTRANCE
Many of the station entrances for the newly built Paris Métro were designed by Art Nouveau architect Hector Guimard. These designs featured amber lights, wrought-iron arches, and railings decorated with whiplash curves.

ENTRANCE TO LES ABBESSES STATION, PARIS

HOUSE INTERIOR
Every detail in the house was designed by Horta, including the marble columns, mosaic floors, and cast iron radiators.

ART NOUVEAU HOUSE
The Belgian architect Victor Horta designed Van Eetvelde House in Brussels for a rich baron. The rooms are arranged around a central octagonal hall. Glass doors lead from the hall to the two main reception rooms – the salon and the dining room.

VAN EETVELDE HOUSE, BRUSSELS

SALON

HALL

DINING ROOM

FACTS AND FIGURES
• Art Nouveau got its name from a French art gallery, opened in 1895.

• Another name for the style was Style Nouille ("noodle style").

• A less ornate version of Art Nouveau developed in Scotland and Vienna.

• The glassware of Emile Gallé (1846–1904) was a product of Art Nouveau.

• Gaudí's cathedral in Barcelona, begun in 1883, is still being built.

CHICAGO

AFTER A FIRE devastated the city in 1871, Chicago, U.S.A. rose high from the ashes. The first skyscrapers were built here, and architects such as Louis Sullivan and Dankmar Adler pioneered new building styles. Frank Lloyd Wright worked in Sullivan's office and would later design stunning buildings of his own.

FISHER BUILDING
Daniel H. Burnham and John W. Root designed several tall buildings in Chicago in the late 19th century. The Fisher Building is a steel-framed structure, built in 1897.

CARSON, PIRIE, SCOTT DEPARTMENT STORE
The two lower floors of this Chicago store, built in 1899-1904, are faced with Sullivan's feathery cast iron work.

ROBIE HOUSE
This is one of the "prairie houses" designed by Frank Lloyd Wright. It was built in 1907-9. The low, horizontal lines and shallow, overhanging roofs are two of his hallmarks.

AUDITORIUM BUILDING
This building by Sullivan and Adler was designed to contain an opera house, offices, and a hotel. It is a tall building for its time (1886-9), but still makes use of traditional, load-bearing walls.

Load-bearing walls

845/860 LAKESHORE DRIVE
By 1949, architect Ludwig Mies van der Rohe had brought a very different style of skyscraper to Chicago. These apartment buildings are based on a steel framework, which is filled with glass.

The steel framework is visible from the outside

THE INTERNATIONAL STYLE

DURING THE 1920s, architects began to build in a style that owed little to the past. They created tall glass-and-steel towers, white concrete houses with flat roofs and long strips of windows, and buildings with no additional and unnecessary decoration. These features are typical of the International Style of architecture, which began in Europe and spread to become the dominant style in cities of the United States.

BAUHAUS,
DESSAU,
GERMANY

Glass
curtain
wall

CONCERT HALL
Finnish architect Alvar Aalto continued to design buildings in the International Style well into the mid-20th century. This concert hall in Helsinki, built in 1958, has curving concrete walls.

BAUHAUS
The Bauhaus was the most influential school of design of the early 20th century. Its buildings at Dessau, with their glass walls revealing a structure of steel and concrete, were designed by the director Walter Gropius in 1925-6.

EINSTEIN TOWER

Sometimes architects used an expressionistic style, exploiting the sculptural possibilities of concrete or plastered brickwork to produce dramatic curves. This building, combining an observatory and a laboratory, was designed by Erich Mendelsohn in 1921.

EINSTEIN TOWER, POTSDAM, GERMANY

FACTS AND FIGURES

• Bauhaus students learned crafts as well as architecture.

• The Bauhaus closed in 1932, and many teachers went to America.

• A "New Bauhaus" was created in Chicago, U.S.A. in 1937.

• A Dutch magazine called De Stijl (meaning "the style") gave its name to the movement.

Clock tower

HILVERSUM TOWN HALL

The architect Willem Dudok, who was influenced by the Dutch "De Stijl" group of artists, designed this town hall. It was completed in 1934. The De Stijl group produced buildings with plain white walls, carefully arranged windows, and details such as coloured tiles.

TOWN HALL, HILVERSUM, HOLLAND

The projecting eaves appear to be unsupported.

The bands of low windows reflect the influence of Frank Lloyd Wright.

Art deco

A RICHLY DECORATED style of architecture emerged in Europe and the United States during the 1920s. It was launched in France, and became known as Art Deco (Arts Décoratifs). The style had a look of sleek elegance. Art Deco buildings often have rounded streamlined edges, sunbursts, and Egyptian motifs.

Arched sunburst

CHRYSLER SPIRE SUNBURST
The semicircular sunbursts of the Chrysler spire are typical of the Art Deco style. This close-up shows them in detail.

CHRYSLER BUILDING
The Chrysler Building is a 319-m (1,047-ft) high office building in New York. It was built in 1928-30 by William van Alen. The steel-and-concrete skyscraper has a striking, tapering spire with sunbursts.

LIFT DOORS
The Chrysler interior has lavish details such as lift doors elegantly inlaid with wood and brass.

HOOVER FACTORY

The white walls, metal-framed windows, and striped corners and cornices of this factory make it one of the finest examples of English Art Deco. It was built in London in 1932-8 by Wallis Gilbert and Partners. Art Deco styles revolutionized industrial architecture.

Tapering window

WINDOW DETAILS

More unusual window shapes, including quarter-circles, are used on this corner of the factory. The tapering shape of the large window is a feature of Art Deco architecture

HOOVER DOORWAY DETAIL

The elaborate tiled and painted decoration above the doorway is influenced by the buildings of ancient Egypt. The pale green colour of the window frames, also popular for roof tiles in this period, is repeated here.

DOORWAY DETAIL

HOOVER FACTORY, LONDON

Striped cornices

Pale green details

HOOVER BUILDING

SKYSCRAPERS

TALL, METAL-FRAMED buildings soaring to the clouds are usually called skyscrapers. The first, the 10-storey Chicago Home Insurance Building, U.S.A. was built in 1883. Safe passenger lifts and better steel structures allowed architects to build higher and higher.

FLATIRON BUILDING
People thought that this building in New York would fall down when it was built in 1902. The triangular skyscraper has 21 storeys, but its narrow corner is only 185 cm (6 ft) wide.

FACTS AND FIGURES

• Elisha Otis developed the first lift with a safety device in 1854.

• Frank Lloyd Wright designed a skyscraper 1,611 m (1 mile) high; it was never built.

• An aeroplane crashed into the Empire State Building in July 1945.

• 50,000 people work in the World Trade Center.

EMPIRE STATE BUILDING
This building was the tallest in the world when it was erected in 1931. It has a steel frame, lined with bricks, and is faced with stone and aluminium panels. The 381-m (1,250-ft) skyscraper was built to a prefabricated design, and took only 15 months to complete.

TV mast

Observation tower

Limestone and granite facing

Art Deco decoration

EMPIRE STATE BUILDING, NEW YORK

NEW YORK SKYSCRAPER DETAILS
The Woolworth Building (1913) has a cathedral-like spire;
the 1930's General Electric Building an Art Deco crown.
The World Trade Center (1971) has less ornate detailing.

CENTURY
TOWER, TOKYO

WOOLWORTH BUILDING

GENERAL ELECTRIC
BUILDING

WORLD TRADE CENTER

Braced
framework

WALL OF GLASS
This skyscaper was
designed by German
architect Mies van der
Rohe in the 1950s. Its
elegance is heightened
by the use of high-
quality materials –
bronze, marble, and
grey-tinted glass.

TWIN TOWERS
Sir Norman Foster's
Century Tower has
two towers (of 19
and 21 storeys)
linked by a central
atrium that floods
the building with
light. There is a
striking, braced
framework, visible
from the outside.

SEAGRAM BUILDING,
NEW YORK

GREAT MODERN HOUSES

SOME OF THE MOST famous modern buildings are one-off houses, which give an architect the chance to create something new. The best examples from the middle of the 20th century show striking uses of materials (especially concrete and glass), dramatic placement of the house in its surroundings, and unusual interior plans.

FARNSWORTH HOUSE
This house was built in the 1940s by Mies van der Rohe. Its design is a simple glass box supported by elegant steel beams. The huge windows allow the inside and outside spaces to merge. The single living area is divided into two by a huge wardrobe.

FALLINGWATER
Fallingwater is perched above a waterfall in Pennsylvania, U.S.A. Frank Lloyd Wright designed the house in the 1930s. It has thick stone walls with sweeping roofs and balconies of concrete.

The flat roof is a common feature of modernism.

Large windows allow clear views of the outside.

The glass "box" contains one large living area.

FARNSWORTH HOUSE, ILLINOIS, U.S.A.

Main living rooms are on the first floor.

Reinforced concrete stilts, or pilotis, support the structure.

OVERHEAD VIEW, VILLA SAVOYE

The ground floor of this house is taken up by garages, and the main living rooms are on the floor above. A gentle ramp rises through the centre of the house to terraces on the upper floors. Concrete screens give privacy and shelter.

Lightweight slabs of concrete form the walls.

VILLA SAVOYE

This house in Poissy, France was built by Le Corbusier in 1929-31. It is constructed of lightweight concrete slabs and rendered (plastered) brickwork. The white walls and columns reflect the elegance of classical Greece.

FACTS AND FIGURES

• Mies van der Rohe's building philosophy was "Less is more".

• Frank Lloyd Wright believed that a building should "grow" out of the earth like a natural organism.

• Le Corbusier is quoted as saying, "A house is a machine for living in".

CONTEMPORARY ARCHITECTURE

MODERN BUILDINGS reflect the freedom of design that new materials and better technology bring. Some architects continue to design in the International Style, building tall steel-and-glass office blocks and apartment houses. Many have explored the sculptural qualities of concrete, and others have turned buildings inside-out, placing pipes, air-conditioning, and services on the outside.

Shell roof covered with tiles

Double-layered glass walls cut out sound.

FACTS AND FIGURES

• A building that reflects its use on the outside is known as "functionalist".

• Post-modernism is a colourful, imaginative style of architecture that rejects simple modernist ideals.

• Philip Johnson's AT&T Headquarters in New York, U.S.A. was the first famous post-modern building.

Opera theatre

Concert hall

SYDNEY OPERA HOUSE
The Danish architect Jørn Utzon designed this structure. It contains both a large concert hall and an opera theatre. It has stunning, shell-like roofs made of concrete ribs covered with gleaming ceramic tiles.

Double staircase

Air-conditioning unit

Escalator

CENTRE GEORGES POMPIDOU, PARIS

CENTRE GEORGES POMPIDOU

Architects Richard Rogers and Renzo Piano put all the services – water pipes, stairways, air-conditioning, and lifts – on the outside of this building. This allows for vast, uninterrupted exhibition areas inside.

POMPIDOU EXTERIOR

The building is criss-crossed by steel lattice-beams. Pipes run up the outsides.

NOTRE DAME DU HAUT, RONCHAMP

The roof has a metal framework.

NOTRE DAME DU HAUT

This French church was designed by Le Corbusier. The curved, concrete walls are pierced with small stained glass windows to throw pools of coloured light into the white interior. The roof is metal and concrete.

20TH-CENTURY CITIES

FROM IMPRESSIVE CENTRES of government to housing for ordinary people in pleasant surroundings, city planning continues to fascinate 20th-century architects. Planned new towns, complete with housing, roads, schools, and services, were first built in England at the turn of the century. Today, planned communities are found across the world.

BOURNVILLE
This town in England was built by a Quaker chocolate manufacturer to house his workers. The houses had generous gardens, so that the occupants could grow food and live in a "green" environment.

Tree-lined roads were built around a central green with shops.

OLD PARLIAMENT
HOUSE, CANBERRA

Central meeting hall

CANBERRA

Australia's specially built capital was begun in 1913 to a design by Walter Burley Griffin. The city is zoned, with different areas for shops, houses, government offices, and so on. Many of the roads radiate out from circular parks, like the spokes of a wheel. The new Parliament House was added in 1988.

The twin towers contain the administrative offices.

NATIONAL CONGRESS
BUILDING,
BRASILIA

The reversed dome of the Chamber of Deputies reflects Brasilia's evening sunshine.

FACTS AND FIGURES

• Seen from the air, Brasilia appears to be planned in the shape of an aircraft.

• Houses in Bournville Garden City had sunken baths – but they were in the kitchen!

• Le Corbusier and Tony Garnier both produced plans for ideal cities, but these were never built.

BRASILIA

Planned on a rural site by Lúcio Costa, Brazil's modern capital features buildings designed by Oscar Niemeyer. These structures, like the Congress Building shown here, are outstanding, but the city had little low-cost housing, forcing people out into the outskirts.

THE FUTURE

ALMOST ANYTHING may be possible in future buildings, from energy-efficient designs to services controlled by computer. Natural energy sources such as wind power and solar heating will be used where the climate allows, and buildings will be insulated with new materials to save energy.

The building is a kilometre (about half a mile) long.

N.M.B. BANK
This is thought to be the world's most energy-efficient building. Glazed panels on the roof collect solar energy for heating and insulated water tanks in the basement recycle waste heat from equipment within the building. The walls are insulated with mineral fibre.

N.M.B. BANK,
NEAR
AMSTERDAM,
HOLLAND

Pentagonal glazed areas collect solar energy.

TURBINE TOWER

A series of turbines is incorporated into this design, so that the building's energy needs can be met by wind power. In winter, sun is let in to warm the tower, and a heat-exchange system heats the cool air. The building absorbs and stores the extra heat generated in the summer.

The building is shaped to encourage the wind to pass through the turbines.

WIND TESTING

A wind tunnel was used to test models of the building and its turbines. This allowed the architects to work out the best shape for both tower and turbines, taking into account the local wind speeds and the effect of nearby buildings on the speed and direction of the wind.

TURBINE TOWER, PLANNED FOR TOKYO, JAPAN

Wind turbine

Service tower

FACTS AND FIGURES

• Sir Norman Foster's Millennium Tower, planned for Tokyo, will soar to 767 m (2,515 ft).

• The United States is planning a permanent space station, *Freedom*.

• Computer-controlled mechanisms will protect future buildings from earthquake damage.

• Materials that use less energy to manufacture will be used more frequently in the future.

REFERENCE SECTION

COMPONENTS OF ARCHITECTURE

THE DETAILS – doors, windows, and arches – can tell us a lot about a building. As structures and fashions change over the years, these features can help to date a building. There are also local variations which are revealed in these key elements.

ARCHES

Large buildings, such as churches and cathedrals, often have many arches, providing clues to the age of a building. Perhaps the most outstanding innovation was the pointed arch in Europe in the 11th century, which paved the way for the Gothic style.

BASKET ARCH
This arch was used in Romanesque buildings up to the 11th century.

LANCET ARCH
This type of slender, pointed arch was used in the later 11th and 12th centuries.

TREFOIL ARCH
This more ornate type of Gothic arch appeared in the 14th century.

TUDOR ARCH
In Britain in the 16th century, arches were often built to this flatter design.

WINDOWS

With the increasing availability of large, flat sheets of clear glass, windows have changed radically over the centuries. In early medieval times, windows often had no glass and were very small. Today, the entire exterior of a building may be glazed.

ANGLO-SAXON WINDOW
Windows in the 10th and 11th centuries were often tiny, unglazed openings.

ROMANESQUE WINDOW
The semicircular head and columns are typical of the Byzantine and Romanesque.

BAROQUE WINDOW
This oeil de boeuf (ox eye) window was used in the 17th and 18th centuries.

MODERN WINDOWS
Plate glass and metal frames allowed the 20th-century "wall of glass".

DOORWAYS

These show a similar development to windows, but often have additional ornament on the jambs (sides) and above the door. They vary in size according to the importance of the building – grand structures, such as churches, cathedrals, and public buildings, usually have large, ornate doorways with carved surrounds.

ROMANESQUE DOORWAY
This Romanesque doorway from the early 12th century has recessed semicircular arches.

GOTHIC DOORWAY
Builders in the 13th century also used recessed arches, but the arches were pointed.

ANCIENT GREEK DOORWAY
The Greeks made little use of arches, so their doorways have a rectangular shape.

RENAISSANCE DOORWAY
Renaissance architects revived the rectangular shape of ancient Greece and Rome.

ANGLO-SAXON DOORWAY
The Saxons often used triangular openings for doorways. The decoration was usually plain.

ART NOUVEAU DOORWAY
At the end of the 19th century, architects experimented with shapes like this elipsoid.

VAULTS

A simple barrel vault is an arched covering in stone or brick – it always looked the same, and was difficult to build strongly in a wide building. The introduction of the pointed arch, together with intersecting ribs, allowed for stronger, wider vaults.

GROIN VAULT
Two intersecting barrel vaults were joined with groins in an X-shape.

RIB VAULT
Gothic builders developed the rib vault, using pointed arches in rectangular spaces.

BARREL VAULT
A simple Romanesque vault, this creates a semi-circular tunnel effect.

FAN VAULT
This ornate version of the rib vault was introduced in the late medieval period.

ROOF STRUCTURES

There are many different designs used for the timbers that support roofs. Their aims, however, are the same: to hold up the roof covering, keep the structure rigid, and minimize the tendency for the roof structure to push the walls of the building apart.

TRUSSED RAFTER
This type could be used over wider spans. It was sometimes boarded over.

ARCH BRACE
The tie beam was replaced with curved timbers in a Gothic arch.

TIE BEAM
This extremely simple construction was used over narrow spans.

HAMMER BEAM
This combines the two previous designs with added hammer beams.

ORNAMENTS

Almost every country and period has its characteristic ornament, and only a small selection can be shown here. Such ornament can appear anywhere on a building – around doorways and windows, in decorative cornices along the tops of walls, and in plasterwork on ceilings. It is often a good clue to the age of the building.

BYZANTINE
Architects of the Byzantine Empire often used a deeply carved "openwork" design.

ROMANESQUE
Buildings in this style are often ornamented. The most common was a simple carved zigzag.

GREEK CARVED FRET
The ancient Greeks used many variations on this fret design or key pattern.

GOTHIC FOLIAGE
Cathedrals and churches of the 13th century are frequently adorned with foliage.

ACANTHUS
Both the Greeks and Romans used this leaf ornament on their buildings.

BALLFLOWERS
This motif belongs to the later Gothic of the 14th century. It is often found around windows.

CLASSICAL ORDERS

The ancient Greeks and Romans based all their decoration on styles called orders. The Greeks had Doric, Ionic, and Corinthian; the Romans added Tuscan and Composite.

CORINTHIAN
The capitals of the Corinthian order are known for their decoration of richly carved acanthus leaves.

DORIC
This was the earliest order. The capitals are simple. The fluted columns do not have separate bases.

TUSCAN
Capitals of the Tuscan order are similar to the Doric, but the columns are plain, not fluted.

IONIC
A noticeable feature of the Ionic order is the twin spiral design of the capitals.

COMPOSITE
Composite capitals resemble Corinthian capitals, but with spiral motifs at each of the corners.

DOMES

Some of the most imposing roofs are in the form of domes. These are usually difficult to build, and the shape depends on whether the priority is to create a striking exterior or to roof a large interior.

HEMISPHERICAL DOME
This dome shape makes an imposing silhouette, but it is difficult to build.

POLYHEDRAL DOME
This solution to roofing an octagonal space was used on Florence Cathedral.

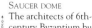

SAUCER DOME
The architects of 6th-century Byzantium built wide, shallow domes covering large interiors.

ONION DOME
The 16th-century St. Basil's cathedral in Moscow has many onion domes, a popular feature on Russian buildings.

TIMELINE

THIS TIMELINE SHOWS where and
when some of the most important
styles of architecture were used,
and how they developed. There is
much similarity in Indian and Far
Eastern buildings over a wide
timespan, whereas there are many
radical changes of style in the
West. In the 20th century, styles
tend to become more international.

1000 B.C.-1 A.D.

CHINESE
MILITARY

Great Wall
of China

Parthenon

KEY
These colours show the geographical
groupings used in the chart.

Far East, India,
and Australia

Americas

Europe

Middle East
and Africa

7000-1000 B.C.

ANCIENT
ANATOLIAN
Turkey

MINOAN
Crete

EGYPTIAN OLD
KINGDOM

SUMERIAN
Middle East

Ziggurat, Ur, Iraq

CLASSICAL
GREEK

NEO-
BABYLONIAN

City gateway,
Babylon

| 1-500 | 500-1000 | | 1100-1200 |

Angkor Wat, Cambodia

| BUDDHIST *India* | NARA *Japan* | | KHMER *Cambodia* |

| 1000-1100 |

Pyramid of the Sun, Mexico

Temple of the Warriors, Mexico

| PRECLASSICAL MESOAMERICAN | | POST-CLASSICAL MAYAN *South America* | |

| CLASSICAL ROMAN | BYZANTINE *East Europe* | NORTH ITALIAN ROMANESQUE | SOUTH ITALIAN ROMANESQUE |

Colosseum, Rome

| | | FRENCH ROMANESQUE | FRENCH GOTHIC |

| | EARLY CHRISTIAN *The Holy Land* | | EARLY MEDIEVAL CRUSADER *Middle East* |

Church of the Nativity, Israel

Krak des Chevaliers, Syria

| | EARLY ISLAMIC *Middle East* | | |

Minaret of Great Mosque of Samarra, Iraq

1200-1300

HINDU-JAIN
India

*Forbidden City,
Beijing*

1400-1500

MING DYNASTY
China

INDIAN
ISLAMIC

*Friday Mosque of
Ahmad Shah, India*

*Machu Picchu,
Peru*

INCA

1500-1600

SOUTH
AMERICAN
BAROQUE

*Reims Cathedral,
France*

EUROPEAN
GOTHIC

1300-1400

HISPANO-
MAGHREBI
ISLAMIC

NORTH
EUROPEAN
RENAISSANCE

ENGLISH
GOTHIC

ITALIAN
GOTHIC

ITALIAN
RENAISSANCE

SPANISH
RENAISSANCE

OTTOMAN

*Salisbury Cathedral,
Britain*

*Milan Cathedral,
Italy*

*Church of St. Andrea,
Mantua, Italy*

*Selimiye Mosque,
Edirne, Turkey*

1600-1700

LATE MOGUL INDIA

Taj Mahal, India

St. Paul's Cathedral, Britain

ENGLISH BAROQUE

FRENCH BAROQUE

SAFAVID *Middle East*

Masjid-i-Shah, Iran

1700-1800

RUSSIAN BAROQUE

Winter Palace, St. Petersburg, Russia

Merchants' Exchange, Philadelphia, U.S.A.

Opera House, Sydney, Australia

1800-1900

EARLY NEO-CLASSICAL

METAL CONSTRUCTION

ART NOUVEAU

BRITISH COLONIAL

1900-

AUSTRALIAN-SCANDINAVIAN

ART DECO

HIGH TECH

INTERNATIONAL STYLE

House of Wonders, Zanzibar, Tanzania

FROM PLAN TO BUILDING

EVERY BUILDING has to be designed. The architect produces a set of plans which the builder can follow and construction is carried out in a strict order – foundations have to be laid before walls can be built, and decoration is the final stage.

PLAN

Drawings are accompanied by notes on materials and construction.

Stairs

Door Window

ELEVATION

PLANS AND ELEVATIONS

The architect produces plans of each floor, showing its dimensions and features, such as stairs, doors, and windows. Elevations are drawings of each side of the building, showing how it will look when built.

Trenches for foundations

Concrete weight-bearing point GROUNDWORKS

GROUNDWORKS

The builder's first job will be to prepare the ground, removing topsoil, making it level, marking out the position of the building, and digging trenches to take the foundations. Concrete is poured in to make the foundations, and pipes are inserted for wires, water, and gas.

SUPERSTRUCTURE

Platforms laid on scaffolding to support workers

Scaffolding

Window frame

SUPERSTRUCTURE
As the walls rise, door and window frames are added, with lintels on top to take the weight of the masonry. Higher still, joists are fitted to take the upper floor. Scaffolding allows access to the roof.

SERVICES
Electrical wiring and plumbing are fitted. Many of the wires and pipes go under the floorboards and behind plasterwork, so they must be put in first.

THE FINISHED BUILDING
After the carpenter has fitted the internal door frames, stairs, and floorboards, the plasterer plasters the walls and ceilings. Then windows can be glazed, doors fitted, and the plumbing and electrical work completed, before decorating begins.

Finished house matches the elevation

The completed house is ready to be occupied.

GREAT ARCHITECTS

LARGE BUILDINGS HAVE ALWAYS required people to plan them and to supervise their construction. But it is only since the Renaissance in Europe that architects have emerged as important people whose names are permanently associated with the buildings they design.

FILIPPO BRUNELLESCHI (1377-1446) Brunelleschi designed the dome of Florence Cathedral. He was one of the first Italian Renaissance architects.	LEON BATTISTA ALBERTI (1404-72) was an Italian writer, painter, musician, and architect. He remodelled several churches, such as Santa Maria Novella in Florence, and designed the Palazzo Rucellai in Florence. He wrote one of the first popular books on architecture.
DONATO BRAMANTE (1444-1514) was an influential Italian architect who brought an imposing, monumental quality to Renaissance buildings. He probably worked on the Ducal Palace at Urbino before designing churches such as Santa Maria Presso San Satiro in Milan.	LEONARDO DA VINCI (1452-1519) was the greatest artist and thinker of the Renaissance. Although he built little or nothing, his influence was great, especially on Bramante. He provided a model for the dome of Milan Cathedral in 1487, and a vast plan for a French city and castle.
MICHELANGELO BUONAROTTI (1475-1564) He is most famous for his paintings on the Sistine Chapel ceiling in the Vatican, but Michelangelo was also a great architect. He added the dome to St. Peter's in Rome, and worked on the Medici chapel in Florence.	SINAN (1491-1588) was a Turkish architect responsible for more than 300 buildings. His mosques had central domes flanked by smaller side domes.

PHILIBERT DE L'ORME (1515-70) was a French Renaissance architect with a talent for original structures and plans. He is famous for his work on the Château de Chenonceaux, and the Tuileries Palace in Paris.

INIGO JONES (1573-1652) was the first English architect to design along classical Renaissance lines. He travelled in Italy before working for James I and Charles I. His buildings in London include the Queen's House, Greenwich; and St. Paul's Church, Covent Garden.

FRANCOIS MANSART (1598-1666) was one of the architects who began to develop the baroque style in France, sometimes combining Renaissance and baroque details in his buildings. He designed the Château de Berny, and built the church of Sainte Marie de la Visitation in Paris.

GIOVANNI LORENZO BERNINI (1599-1680) Bernini started work as a sculptor before designing buildings in the baroque style. Most of his buildings are churches and palaces in Rome, such as San Andrea al Quirinale, and the Piazza in front of St. Peter's.

FRANCESCO BORROMINI (1599-1667) was one of the first Italian baroque architects. He trained as a stonecarver before designing buildings, such as San Carlo alle Quattro Fontane in Rome, which show a dramatic use of shapes like triangles and curves. He also designed the Palazzo Falconieri, Rome.

LOUIS LE VAU (1612-70) worked with interior designer Charles le Brun to create elaborate baroque town houses. He designed the Château of Vaux le Vicomte.

CHRISTOPHER WREN (1631-1723) is the most famous English classical architect. After the Great Fire of London (1666), he designed 51 new churches and rebuilt St. Paul's Cathedral. He is famous for his alterations to the royal palace at Hampton Court.

JULES HARDOUIN MANSART (1646-1707) was the great-nephew of François Mansart and France's first fully fledged baroque architect. He designed various châteaux before becoming architect to King Louis XIV, for whom he remodelled parts of the sumptuous palace of Versailles.

BERNHARD FISHER VON ERLACH (1656-1723)
An Austrian baroque architect, Von Erlach trained in Rome and worked mainly in Vienna. He is famous for rich palaces, such as the Palace of the Hungarian Guard, Vienna, and the Clam Galles Palace, Prague.

NICHOLAS HAWKSMOOR (1661-1736)
was an English architect who assisted both Sir Christopher Wren and Sir John Vanbrugh, working on such buildings as St. Paul's Cathedral and Castle Howard. His baroque style, greatly influenced by Wren, is evident in his six London churches.

SIR JOHN VANBRUGH (1664-1726)
was a British army officer and playwright before an architect. His first building was the enormous, baroque Castle Howard, designed for a friend. Vanbrugh also designed Blenheim Palace, becoming the best known architect of English baroque.

KARL FRIEDRICH SCHINKEL (1781-1841)
was the greatest German architect of the neo-classical style. His buildings use Greek and Roman details, and include Berlin's Altes Museum and New Guard House.

A.W.N. PUGIN (1812-52)
was the English architect who was a great advocate of the Gothic revival. He was famous for his books explaining the Gothic style, for his Gothic churches, and for designing the rich details of the interior of the Houses of Parliament in London.

J.L.C. GARNIER (1825-98)
was a little-known French architect of the Second Empire until he won the competition to design the great opera house that was to be the focal point of Paris. After the Opéra was finished in 1875, he went on to design casinos at Monte Carlo and Vittel.

ANTONI GAUDI (1852-1926)
was a Catalan architect with a unique style. His buildings feature sculptural roofs and mosaic decorations. His most famous work is Barcelona's unfinished Sagrada Familia church.

LOUIS SULLIVAN (1856-1924)
was an influential Chicago architect who was a great pioneer of the skyscraper. His buildings, such as the Carson Pirie Scott Store and the Auditorium Building in Chicago, are modern in that their structure can be seen from the outside, but they are covered in beautiful ornament.

VICTOR HORTA (1861-1947)
was a Belgian architect who created
the Art Nouveau style. In a group of
houses and public buildings in Brussels
he developed the use of elegant
whiplash curves in a style known for
its extravagance. This can be seen in
the Van Eetvelde and Tassel houses.

FRANK LLOYD WRIGHT (1867-1959)
was the best-known modern
American architect. He
designed a variety of
structures from numerous
houses to factories
and public
buildings.

CHARLES RENNIE MACKINTOSH
(1868-1928)
Mackintosh was a Scottish architect
who developed an individual version
of the Art Nouveau style based upon
straight lines. His best known-work is
in Glasgow, in buildings such as the
School of Art and Willow Tea Rooms.

SIR EDWIN LUTYENS (1869-1944)
was a British architect who was one of
the last in the early 20th century to
use traditional motifs from classical
design – and the old construction
methods that went with them. He was
famous for his country houses and for
the planning of New Delhi, India.

WALTER GROPIUS (1883-1969)
was a modern architect and a teacher.
He was a founder of the Bauhaus
school and designed
the Bauhaus
buildings at
Dessau in
Germany.

LUDWIG MIES VAN DER ROHE
(1886-1969)
One of the fathers of modern
architecture, this German architect
designed steel and glass buildings,
summing up his theory that "less is
more". He believed that a building
should reflect its function.

LE CORBUSIER (1887-1965)
was the name used by the important
Swiss-French architect Charles
Edouard Jeanneret. He developed
many of the key features of modern
building, such as the use of glass and
concrete, and the idea of a whole
community – homes, shops, and
services – housed in one building.

KENZO TANGE (b.1913)
is known as the Grand Old Man of
modern Japanese architecture. His
buildings include the stadia for the
Tokyo Olympic Games, and the twin
skyscraper towers of the City Hall at
Shinjuku, Tokyo, completed in the
late 1980s. He has also been an
influential city planner.

Resources

Whenever you are visiting an unfamiliar town, look out for the local Tourist Information Centre. Such centres usually have a wide range of information and publicity material about local buildings, especially those that are open to the public. Another useful source is likely to be the local museum, where there may be both publicity material and staff who are able to give information about local history, buildings, and architecture.

UNITED KINGDOM

Abriachan Croft Museum
The Old School House
Abriachan
Inverness
IV3 6LB

Architectural Association
34 Bedford Square
London WC1

Avoncroft Museum of Buildings
Redditch Road
Stoke Heath
Bromsgrove, Worts.

Black Country Museum
Tipton Road
Dudley
West Midlands
DY1 4SO

British Museum
Great Russell St
London WC1

Building Centre
26 Store Street
London WC1E 7BT

Building of Bath Museum
Countess of Huntingdons
Chapel
The Vineyards
The Paragon
Bath, Avon

Chiltern Open Air Museum
Newland Park
Chalfont St Giles
Buckinghamshire
HP8 4AD

English Heritage
Fortress House
23 Saville Row
London W1X 1RB

Geffrye Museum
Kingsland Road
London E2 8EA

Historic Houses Association
2 Chester Street
London SW1X 7BB

Ironbridge Gorge Museum
Ironbridge
Telford
Shropshire
TF8 7AW

Morwellham Quay
Morwellham
Tavistock
Devon

Museum of East Anglian Life
Stowmarket
Suffolk
IP14 1DL

Museum of London
London Wall
London WC2

National Trust
36 Queen Annes Gate
London SW1H 9AS

**New Lanark
Conservation Village**
New Lanark Mills
Lanark ML11 9DB

Old Merchant's Houses
South Quay
Great Yarmouth
Norfolk

**Pickford's House Social
History Museum**
41 Friar Gate
Derby

**Port Sunlight Heritage
Centre**
95 Greendale Road
Port Sunlight

**Royal Institute of British
Architects**
66 Portland Place
London W1N 4AD

Ryedale Folk Museum
Hutton-Le-Hole
York Y06 6UA

Science Museum
Exhibition Road
South Kensington
London SW7

**Sir John Soane's
Museum**
13 Lincoln's Inn Fields
London

Stained Glass Museum
The Cathedral
Ely
Cambridgeshire

**Victoria and Albert
Museum**
Cromwell Road
London
SW7 2RL

**Weald and Downland
Museum**
Singleton
West Sussex

Welsh Folk Museum
St Fagans
Cardiff

AUSTRALIA

National Trust Offices:

6 Gells Circuit
Deakin, ACT 2600

52 Temira Crescent
Darwin, NT 0800

Observatory Hill
Sydney, NSW 2000

Old Government House
George Street
Brisbane, Qld 4000

PO Box 61
Rundle Mall
Adelaide, SA 5000

Brisbane/Campbell
Streets
Hobart
Tasmania 7000

Tasma Terrace
Parliament Place
Melbourne
Victoria 3000

4 Havelock Street
West Perth
WA 6005

NEW ZEALAND

**Queen Elizabeth The
Second National Trust**
Colenso House
138 The Terrace
Wellington

Glossary

ARCH
Structure, usually curved, over an opening. An arch is designed so that it can be supported only from the sides.

ARCHITECT
Person who designs buildings and supervises their construction.

ARCHITRAVE
In classical architecture, the lowest part of the entablature. Or, the moulded surround of a window or a door.

BAILEY
The courtyard, or ward, of a castle.

BAROQUE
Late Renaissance (17th- and 18th-century) style, typified by bold, highly elaborate decoration.

BARREL VAULT
Vault with a continuous, semicircular section, like a tunnel.

BASILICA
Originally a Roman public hall consisting of a large room with side aisles. Later adapted for Christian churches.

BUTTRESS
Masonry projection from a wall, often helping to support a vault or roof.

CAPITAL
The upper section of a column, often carved.

CAST IRON
Iron shaped by pouring the molten metal into a pre-formed mould.

CEMENT
Mixture of clay and limestone, heated and ground to a powder.

CHOIR
The eastern area of a Christian church or cathedral, normally occupied by the choir and the clergy; also called quire or chancel.

CLASSICAL
Style of architecture used in ancient Greece and Rome, and imitated in later periods.

COLUMN
A vertical post-like support. Usually consists of three parts: a base, a shaft (usually circular or polygonal), and a capital at the top.

CONCRETE
Mixture, usually of cement, sand, gravel, and water. It can be poured into a mould where it sets hard.

CORBEL
Stone blocks, sticking out from a wall, used to support part of a building, such as a roof or floor timbers.

CORINTHIAN
One of the classical orders, typified by the acanthus-leaf decoration on the capital and fluted columns.

CORNICE
In classical architecture, the upper part of the entablature. Or, the area where the wall and ceiling join, decorated with plaster mouldings.

CRUCKS
Two curved timbers, arranged in an inverted V-shape to form the framework of a building.

CRYPT
Basement area in a building, especially a church or cathedral.

DOME
A curved solid roof, usually circular or polygon in its plan.

DORIC
One of the classical orders, typified by plain capitals and fluted columns without bases.

DRUM
Cylindrical structure below a dome. Gives the dome extra height and allows for the inclusion of windows to light the interior.

EAVES
Lower part of a roof, where it overhangs the face of the wall.

ENTABLATURE
In classical architecture, section of wall just above the capitals of the columns, made up of the architrave, frieze, and cornice supported by a colonnade.

FACADE
The face or elevation of a building.

FAN VAULT
Style of vaulting used in England in the 16th century, in which the ribs are of equal length and form a fan shape.

FORUM
The public open space, for social, civic or market purposes, found in every Roman town.

FOUNDATIONS
The underground section of a building, which supports the weight above ground.

GABLE
Triangular part of a wall between the sides of a pitched roof.

GARGOYLE
Grotesque or humorous carving sticking out from the side of a building. They often disguise a water spout.

GOTHIC
Style of architecture fashionable in western Europe in the medieval period, typified by the use of pointed arches.

GROIN VAULT
Vault with curved edges that mark the places where the intersecting surfaces meet.

HALF-TIMBERED
Type of building with a wooden frame and the spaces filled in with wattle and daub, brick, or other material.

IONIC
One of the classical orders, typified by capitals decorated with a spiral motif.

JAMB
The side of a doorway or a window.

JOIST
Beam supporting a floor.

KEYSTONE
Central stone at the top of an arch.

KING POST
Vertical roof timber joining the tie beam to the ridge above.

LANCET
Narrow, sharp pointed arch or window common in early Gothic buildings.

LINENFOLD
A type of ornament, imitating folded linen, carved on timber panels.

LINTEL
Horizontal beam, made of wood or stone, spanning the top of a window or doorway.

LOUVRE
Slat that can be angled to admit air, while preventing rain or direct sunlight from entering the building.

MACHIOLATION
In a castle, a projecting parapet with openings in the floor, through which missiles were dropped.

MANSARD ROOF
Roof with a steep lower slope and a more gently sloping upper section, named after the French architect Mansart.

MASONRY
Usually, building work in stone; sometimes the term includes work in brick or concrete.

MIHRAB
A prayer-niche in mosques oriented towards Mecca. It first appeared in the early 8th century.

MINARET
Slim tower forming part of a mosque, from which an official called a muezzin calls the faithful to prayer.

MORTAR
Material made usually from cement, sand, and lime. It is used as a bond between bricks or stone.

MOSAIC
Decorative design made up of small squares of coloured stone or glass.

MOTTE
The earth mound of an early medieval castle.

MOULDINGS
Decorative profile given to a projecting part, such as a ceiling cornice.

NAVE
The western arm of a Christian church.

NICHE
Recess in a wall, often specially designed to accommodate a statue.

ORDERS
The styles of classical architecture, defined by the designs of their columns and entablatures. The three Greek orders were the Doric, Ionic, and Corinthian. The Romans added Tuscan and Composite.

PARAPET
The part of a wall above the gutter, which is sometimes decorated with battlements or other designs.

PEDIMENT
In classical architecture, a triangular section of wall above the entablature. Can also be a semicircular shape.

PENDENTIVE
Curved triangular surface formed to support a circular dome over a square structure.

PIER
Solid masonry support for an arch or bridge.

PILE
Shaft of wood or concrete which is driven into the ground as part of the foundations of the building.

PILOTIS
Posts or "stilts" raising a building off the ground.

PLINTH
The projecting base of a building. Or, the lowest part of a column base.

PORTICO
Entrance porch supported by a row of decorative columns.

PREFABRICATION
Making of parts of a building in advance, so that they can later be assembled on site.

QUADRANGLE
Four-sided enclosure or courtyard surrounded by buildings on all sides.

QUOINS
Corner stones, usually the largest in a wall.

REINFORCED CONCRETE
Concrete strengthened by means of steel rods.

RENAISSANCE
The period during which the classical style of architecture was reintroduced in Europe; the 15th and 16th centuries in most places.

RIBBED VAULT
Vault in which the intersections of the surfaces are marked by projecting bands of stone that form arches.

ROMANESQUE
Style of architecture, based on the Roman style. It was popular in Europe between the 9th and 12th centuries.

RUSTICATION
A method of forming stonework with roughened surfaces and recessed joints, principally employed in Renaissance buildings. It gives a rich, bold texture to an exterior wall.

ROSE WINDOW
Circular window with patterned tracery arranged like the spokes of a wheel, often used in Gothic cathedrals.

SCREEN
A partition or enclosure of iron, stone or wood, often carved.

SHAFT
The section of a column between the base and the capital.

SKYSCRAPER
Very tall building, usually with a steel framework.

SPIRE
Tall, tapering structure on top of a tower, usually found on Gothic-style churches.

STUCCO
Fine plaster used for decoration in low relief.

STUPA
Buddhist sacred building, usually in the form of an earth mound clad with brick or stone.

TEMPIETTO
Compact circular or temple-like structures erected in the grounds of country houses.

TIE BEAM
Horizontal beam forming part of the structure of a roof. It connects two walls, preventing them from moving apart.

TRACERY
The ornamental work in the upper part of a window, screen, or panel, or used decoratively in blank arches and vaults.

TRANSEPTS
Parts of a church or cathedral built at right-angles to the nave and choir, often housing small chapels.

TYMPANUM
The triangular surface bounded by the sloping and horizontal cornices of a pediment.

VAULT
Arched masonry covering over a building.

WATTLE AND DAUB
Walling material consisting of mud or dung plastered over a criss-crossing arrangement of twigs.

WROUGHT IRON
Form of iron with little carbon. It is softer than iron or steel.

ZIGGURAT
A high, stepped pyramid, which formed an important element in ancient Mesopotamian temple complexes.

Index